MATHEMATICS AND MENTAL GROWTH

Also by Irving Adler

COLOR IN YOUR LIFE
DUST
THE ELEMENTARY MATHEMATICS OF THE ATOM
FIRE IN YOUR LIFE
HOT AND COLD
HOW LIFE BEGAN
INSIDE THE NUCLEUS
MAGIC HOUSE OF NUMBERS
MAN-MADE MOONS
MONKEY BUSINESS: HOAXES IN THE NAME OF SCIENCE
A NEW LOOK AT ARITHMETIC
A NEW LOOK AT GEOMETRY
THE NEW MATHEMATICS
PROBABILITY AND STATISTICS FOR EVERYMAN
THE SECRET OF LIGHT
SEEING THE EARTH FROM SPACE
THE STARS: STEPPINGSTONES INTO SPACE
THE SUN AND ITS FAMILY
THINKING MACHINES
TIME IN YOUR LIFE
TOOLS IN YOUR LIFE
THE TOOLS OF SCIENCE
WEATHER IN YOUR LIFE
WHAT WE WANT OF OUR SCHOOLS
THE REASON WHY BOOKS (*with Ruth Adler*)

IRVING ADLER

Mathematics
and Mental Growth

**WITH DIAGRAMS BY RUTH ADLER
AND ELLEN VIERECK**

THE JOHN DAY COMPANY
New York

Library of Congress Catalog Card Number: 68–15246

Contents

Foreword

A revolution in the teaching of mathematics has been going on for about ten years. This revolution does not consist of merely tinkering with the course of study by removing certain topics and replacing them with others. It involves also a revolution in educational philosophy arising from a reexamination of these fundamental questions:

What is the nature of the learning process?

What are the purposes of teaching mathematics?

Is the teaching of mathematics keeping pace with the changing character of mathematics and of society?

To whom shall we teach mathematics?

What shall we teach them?

This book is offered as a contribution to the discussion of these questions.

The first two chapters deal with the nature of the learning process. Chapter 1 is a critical evaluation of the educational philosophy of Jean Jacques Rousseau and its influence on contemporary education. Chapter 2 is an examination of the developmental psychology of Jean Piaget and its implications for the teaching of mathematics.

Chapter 3 deals with the nature of mathematics. It is a survey of the changes that have taken place in mathematics during recent decades. The schools must take these changes into account if they want to teach twentieth-century mathematics that is relevant for twentieth-century society.

During the first few years of the revolution in school mathematics, it affected only the course of study of the superior student. We are only now beginning to study its significance for the courses being studied by the average student and by the low achiever. Chapter 4 explains why the new mathematics should be taught to all students, and not only to the superior student. Chapter 5 explains, by using specific examples, how this can be done for the low achiever.

The revolution in school mathematics has only just begun. The changes in the curriculum that have been made during the last decade will be deepened and extended during the next few decades. The last three chapters of the book consider what further changes should be made now to pave the way for the curriculum of the future. Chapter 6 is a critical evaluation of the report of the Cambridge Conference on School Mathematics, which tried to forecast the direction that curriculum change should take during the next thirty years. Chapter 7 makes specific proposals for improving the teaching of geometry in the high school. Chapter 8 demonstrates the importance in modern mathematics of the concept of a mathematical group, and shows how this concept can be built up gradually, starting with the first grade.

Most of the chapters of the book are based on talks that I have given at conferences of mathematics teachers. All except two have already appeared in print as articles in professional journals. Chapter 3 was the keynote address at the 1961 conference in Washington, D.C., of state supervisors of mathematics, called by the United States Office of Education of the Department of Health, Education and Welfare. It was published in *The Mathematics Teacher* in October 1962. Chapter 4 was the luncheon address at the 1962 national convention in San Francisco of the National Council of Teachers of Mathematics. It was printed in *The Mathematics Teacher* in November 1963 under the title "Some Thoughts About Curriculum Revision." Chapter 2 was the luncheon address at the 1966 Conference of the Minnesota Council of Teachers of Mathematics, and was printed in *The Arithmetic Teacher* in November 1966 and in *The Mathematic Teacher* in December 1966. Chapter 6 was the banquet address at the 1965 Northwest Mathematics Conference, and was printed in both *The Arithmetic Teacher* and *The Mathematics Teacher* in March 1966. Chapter 7 is based on a talk given at conferences of teachers in Maine, New Hampshire, Texas, Missouri, Illinois, California, and New York. It was published in *The Mathematics Teacher* in March 1968. Chapter 8 is a talk that was given at conferences of teachers in California, Connecticut, Illinois, and Virginia. Chapters 2, 3, 4, 6, 7 and 8 are reproduced here with the permission of the National Council of Teachers of Mathematics. Chapter 5 was an article in the *NEA Journal* of February 1965, and is reproduced here with the permission of the National Education Association.

Chapter 1 is published here for the first time. The quotations from Rousseau that occur in it are taken from the E. P. Dutton edition of *Emile,* translated by Barbara Foxley, and the E. P. Dutton edition of *The Social Contract, and Discourses* translated by G. D. H. Cole. I wish to thank the E. P. Dutton Company for giving me permission to quote from these translations.

1.] Rousseau and the Concept of the Natural Man

MANY of the characteristic features of modern education have their roots in the educational theories of the French writer and publicist Jean Jacques Rousseau. These theories, in turn, have their roots in the social developments of his day which led to the emergence of modern industrial society and democratic government. An understanding of Rousseau's theories, their origin, and their consequences, will help us separate the true from the false in what educators think today, and the good from the bad in what the schools do.

Jean Jacques Rousseau, son of a watchmaker, was born in Geneva in 1712. In his early career he was an engraver's apprentice, then a vagabond, a poet, and a musician. In 1750 he was catapulted to international fame when his "Discourse on the Moral Effects of the Arts and Sciences" won first prize in an essay contest sponsored by the Academy of Dijon. The views he expressed in this essay were elaborated in his later works. His political essays *The Origin of Inequality Among Men* and *The Social Contract* played a part in the democratic revolt against autocracy in government. His novel *The New Heloise* and his autobiography, *Confessions,* stimulated the romantic revolt against classicism in literature. His *Emile* initiated the naturalist revolt against formalism in education.

Rousseau's Views on Education

Emile is written in a hybrid form. It is both an essay and a novel. Rousseau, writing as an imaginary tutor who has complete responsibility for the education of the boy Emile, describes how he guided his development from infancy to manhood. At the same time, he expresses freely his views on all subjects that have a bearing on education. In this way Rousseau himself makes clear the intimate connection between his theory of education and his views on human nature and society.

"God makes all things good," says Rousseau. "Man meddles with them and they become evil." This is the basic idea underlying all of Rousseau's views on society and education. Man is naturally good, he believes. Nature "does everything for the best." ". . . The first impulses of nature are always right; there is no original sin in the human heart. . . ." But, he says, human nature is imprisoned, warped, and corrupted by civilization. To educate the child, he concludes, remove the hampering restrictions of social convention. Do everything to encourage the development of the child's natural tendencies, which are inherently good.

There are three factors that work together in the education of the child, he says. ". . . Education comes to us from nature, from men, or from things. The inner growth of our organs and faculties is the education of nature." Since nature is the only one of these three factors that is "wholly beyond our control," it must be the dominant one. The goal of education "is the goal of nature." Therefore education consists of those activities that foster the "natural" growth of the child.

If the teacher's chief function is to stimulate the development of the child's natural powers, obviously he must know what these powers are. So the first requirement for a good teacher is to study the nature of the child. "Begin," he says, "by making a more careful study of your scholars."

Launching his own study of child nature, Rousseau concludes first that a child must not be viewed as a miniature adult. "Childhood has its own ways of seeing, thinking, and feeling; nothing is more foolish than to try and substitute our ways. . . ." In his development from infancy to manhood, the child passes through several qualitatively different stages of growth. In each stage his powers and requirements are different. His ways of learning vary from stage to stage. Therefore methods of teaching must vary from stage to stage.

Recognizing that children are different from adults, he insists that child life and childish activities be respected. Because the high rate of mortality of children in his day made it highly uncertain whether a child would live to be an adult, he condemns "that cruel education which sacrifices the present to an uncertain future." "Love childhood, indulge its sports, its pleasures, its delightful instincts." For the young boy the emphasis is largely on physical activity. "Exercise his body, his limbs, his senses, his strength, but keep his mind idle as long as you can."

Because he believes in the soundness of "natural" impulses and in the sanctity of childhood, Rousseau would limit the education of the child to what he wants and needs *as a child*. "A man must know many things which seem useless to a child, but need the child learn, or can he indeed learn, all that the man must know? Try to teach the child what is of use to a child and you will find that it takes all his time." Children will learn, he says, "only what they perceive to be of real and present value, either for use or enjoyment. . . ." At the same time, Rousseau does not rely on the child's spontaneously choosing his own goals. It is the teacher's function to manipulate the influences surrounding the child in such a way that the child adopts the teacher's goals as his own. "No doubt," Rousseau says, "he ought only to do what he wants, but he ought to want to do nothing but what you want him to do. He should never take a step you haven't foreseen, nor utter a word you could not foretell." The initiative remains with the teacher. "We must . . . choose what to teach as well as when to teach it."

Although Rousseau would give free rein to the child's "natural" impulses, he is not advocating a soft education. He warns against overprotection which prolongs the child's weakness. Train children, he says, "to endure extremes of temperature, climate, and condition, hunger, thirst, and weariness." Moreover, freedom for the child should not become indulgence of all his whims and childish tyranny over adults. He was against spoiling children. "Do you know the surest way to make your child miserable? Let him have everything he wants." ". . . Give children more real liberty and less power . . . let them do more for themselves and demand less of others."

When it becomes necessary to punish a child, arrange things, Rousseau advises, so that the child is punished not by you but by the natural consequences of his own actions. When he is punished by the natural course of events, he learns the connection between cause and effect. But if *you* punish him, he merely learns to resent your interference. ". . . Children should never receive punishment merely as such; it should always come as the natural consequence of their fault." "Let his unreasonable wishes meet with physical obstacles only, or the punishment which results from his own actions." "Let him early find upon his proud neck the heavy yoke which nature has imposed upon us, the heavy yoke of necessity, under which every finite being must bow."

Rousseau's advocacy of natural punishments is closely related to his emphasis on direct experience as the basis for effective learning. He is sharply critical of that formal type of verbal learning in which memory takes the place of understanding and words are divorced from their meaning. He returns to this theme again and again. "True education," he insists, "consists less in precept than in practice." "Give your scholar no verbal lessons; he should be taught by experience alone." ". . . Your lessons should always be in deeds rather than words." "In any study whatsoever the symbols are of no value without the idea of the things symbolized." "As a general rule—never substitute the symbol for the thing signified, unless it is impossible to show the thing itself; for the child's attention is so taken up with the symbol that he will forget what it signifies."

Rousseau is so fearful of meaningless verbalism that he proposes a deliberate delaying, if not complete exclusion, of verbal learning. When he discusses the very young child, he urges the parent not to "hurry him into speech; he will learn to talk when he feels the want of it." When he outlines his views on the education of the pre-adolescent, he boasts that "Emile will not learn anything by heart." Moreover, there will be no great effort to teach him to read. "Reading," Rousseau says, "is the curse of childhood." "Emile at twelve years old, will hardly know what a book is. . . . When reading is of use to him, I admit he must learn to read, but till then he will only find it a nuisance."

Rousseau's stress on the educational value of direct experience leads him naturally to a laboratory and field-work approach to the study of science. "Measure, count, weigh, compare," he urges. ". . . Our first teachers in natural philosophy are our feet, hands and eyes." The study of mathematics, too, should start with the manipulation of concrete materials. Spatial relations should be discovered by experiment, before they are proved by reasoning. "Let us transform our sensations into ideas, but do not let us jump all at once from the objects of sense to objects of thought. The latter are attained by means of the former. Let the senses be the only guide for the first workings of reason." Here again, he extends his objection to meaningless verbalism into a policy of deliberate withholding of the written word. "No book but the world," he says, "no teaching but that of fact. The child who reads ceases to think, he only reads. He is acquiring words, not knowledge."

One of the important goals Rousseau hopes to achieve through the teaching of science is the cultivation of independence of thought. To realize this goal, the child must be allowed to think things through for himself. "Teach your scholar to observe the phenomena of nature," he advises. "You will soon rouse his curiosity, but if you would have it grow, do not be in too great a hurry to satisfy this curiosity. Put the problems before him and let him solve them himself. Let him know nothing because you have told him, but because he has learnt it for himself. Let him not be taught science, let him discover it. If ever you substitute authority for reason he will cease to reason; he will be a mere plaything of other people's thoughts."

Rousseau values the laboratory and field-work approach to science, too, for the opportunities they offer for physical training and the development of manual skill. "The most obvious advantage of these slow and laborious inquiries," he says, "is this: the scholar, while engaged in speculative studies, is actively using his body, gaining suppleness of limb, and training his hands to labor so that he will be able to make them useful when he is a man." He considers this important because he believes every man should be taught to earn his living through the exercise of some manual skill.

The education of Emile was to be the unfolding of the "natural man." To give this "natural man" the living space he needed, where he could run, jump, play, explore, inquire, and work, without interference from the restricting and corrupting influences of human society, he was brought up in the country. Rousseau did not think this stood in the way of Emile's acquiring a knowledge of human relations, because he would not be ready for such knowledge for some time. According to Rousseau, the social relations of man arise out of sex feeling. "As soon as a man needs a companion he is no longer an isolated creature, his heart is no longer alone. All his relations with his species, all the affections of his heart, come into being along with this." So, until Emile's sexual awakening, his "knowledge is confined to nature and things. The very name of history is unknown to him. . . . He knows the essential relations between men and things, but nothing of the moral relations between man and man." Puberty, according to Rousseau, is the child's gateway into social life. It opens up a new stage in his growth when moral training begins to be important. The basis of this moral training is the adolescent's feeling of sympathy for his fellow men, a feeling that comes into existence, Rousseau believes, as a manifestation of the newly awakened sex instinct. Nevertheless, in apparent contradiction to this belief, Rousseau does outline a procedure for introducing the pre-adolescent, too, to social problems and social relations. During the manual training stage of Emile's education, he takes him on visits to many workshops. Through these excursions Emile gets acquainted with the tools of various crafts, and at the same time learns about the economic interdependence of men. "Thus the idea of social relations is gradually developed in the child's mind, before he can really be an active member of human society. Emile sees that to get tools for his own use, other people must have theirs, and that he can get in exchange what he needs and they possess."

Up to this point, Rousseau has talked only of the education of boys. But now Emile, grown into young manhood, will soon be ready for marriage. Rousseau considers what kind of mate Emile should have, and in this connection expresses his views on the education of girls. These views are all based on the premise that woman is by nature subordinate to man. Inequality between the sexes, he says, "is not of man's making; or at any rate it is not the result of mere prejudice, but of reason." "When once it is proved that men and women are and ought to be unlike in constitution and in temperament, it follows that their education must be different." "A woman's education," he concludes, "must therefore be planned in relation to man. To be pleasing in his sight, to win his respect and love, to train him in childhood, to tend him in manhood, to counsel and console, to make his life pleasant and happy, these are the duties of woman for all time, and this is what she should be taught while she is young." He therefore condemns the admission of both sexes to the same occupations. A woman's place is in the home, and her education revolves around the domestic arts. He is a firm believer in the intellectual inferiority of women. "The search for abstract and speculative truths, for principles and axioms in science, for all that tends to wide generalization, is beyond a woman's grasp; their studies should be thoroughly practical." Nevertheless, within child. On the other hand, he says the teacher should select and control every experience of the child, and predetermine its outcome. The child, he says, "should never take a step you haven't foreseen, nor utter a word you could not foretell." On the one hand he says you cannot teach the young boy about society until after he has matured sexually. On the other hand, he proceeds to do what he says you cannot do by taking Emile to workshops where he can learn about the division of labor, the exchange of commodities, and the economic interdependence of men. It is customary for critics of Rousseau to dismiss these contradictions as the products of his emotional and erratic character. This is a superficial view that prevents a real understanding of his ideas. Actually there is a logic behind his contradictions, and the meaning of his contradictions is the key to an understanding of his ideas as a whole. We shall find this key when we examine his ideas about society.

Rousseau lived at a time when great tensions were building up in the body of French society. The country was ruled by the nobility and clergy, living in idleness, luxury and corruption. More than ninety percent of the people lived on the land, where they labored endlessly to pay taxes and feudal dues. Two-thirds of what they produced from the soil was consumed by taxes. The oppressive feudal dues included land rents and personal service in the army, on the roads, and on the estates of the nobility. The peasant longed for a free life on his own piece of land. In the towns, manufacturing and commerce were growing, but were hampered at every turn by feudal restrictions on trade. The manufacturer, the merchant, and the artisan wanted a free market for their wares. Within the shell of feudal society a new social order of peasants, artisans, merchants and manufacturers was taking shape. In this order, social relations were based on market relations rather than feudal obligations. The new order generated its own system of values in which the ideals of personal liberty and democratic government played an important part. Tensions mounted as the growing needs of the new order came into conflict with the practices of the old. Eleven years after Rousseau died these tensions exploded in the great French Revolution. Rousseau was the prophet of this revolution, the spokesman for the new order, giving voice to the strivings of the people. The revolutionary democratic content of Rousseau's ideas is clearly expressed in his opinions about the French ruling class and its way of life, his theory of property rights, his ideal of the good life, and his theory of government.

Rousseau had no respect for kings and aristocrats. He made clear his opinion of their abilities when he said, "He who loses his crown and lives without it, is more than a king; from the rank of a king, which may be held by a coward, a villain, or madman, he rises to the rank of a man, a position few can fill." He showed how he felt about their privileges when he said, ". . . it is plainly contrary to the law of nature that . . . the privileged few should gorge themselves with superfluities, while the starving multitude are in want of the bare necessities of life." "The man who eats in idleness what he has not himself earned, is a thief. . . ." He showed what he thought about their government when he said, ". . . in monarchies those who rise to the top are most often merely petty blunderers, petty swindlers, and petty intriguers, whose petty talents cause them to get into the highest positions at court. . . ." Conceding that the wars of republics may be more cruel than the wars of monarchies, he said, "But if the wars of kings are less cruel, their peace is terrible; better be their foe than their subject." He refuted the claim of the aristocrats that they ruled for the common good. ". . . The higher classes," he said, "which claim to be useful to the rest are really only seeking their own welfare at the expense of others." They organized societies and wrote laws, he said, "which bound new fetters on the poor, and gave new powers to the rich; which irretrievably destroyed natural liberty, eternally fixed the law of property and inequality, converted clever usurpation into unalterable right, and, for the advantage of a few ambitious individuals, subjected all mankind to perpetual labor, slavery, and wretchedness." His estimate of the feudal society in which he lived was summed up in the ringing words of *The Social Contract:* "Man is born free, and everywhere he is in chains."

Rousseau gave thought to the question of the origin of property rights. The conclusion he came to is clearly the articulate expression of the dumb strivings of the land-hungry peasant. He said, ". . . it is impossible to conceive how property can come from anything but manual labor. . . . It is the husbandman's labor alone that, giving him a title to the produce of the ground he has tilled, gives him a claim also to the land itself, at least till harvest." The outlook of the peasant multitudes is also evident in Rousseau's conception of the good life. He said, "If there is any safe and lawful way of living without intrigues, without lawsuits, without dependence on others, it is, I admit, to live by the labor of our hands, by the cultivation of our own land." ". . . That is all a wise man requires, a wife and land of his own." True liberty, he believed, is the freedom of the independent farmer or artisan acting alone. "Your freedom and your power," he said, "extend as far and no farther than your natural strength; anything more is but slavery, deceit and trickery."

His identification with the way of life of the common people was expressed in a variety of value judgments. He thought the simple life of the laborer and peasant more wholesome than the luxury and refinement of the ruling class. "Richness of apparel may proclaim the man of fortune, and elegance the man of taste; but true health and manliness are known by different signs. It is under the homespun of the laborer, and not beneath the gilt and tinsel of the courtier, that we should look for strength and vigor of body." Moreover, the simple life was aesthetically superior, too. ". . . Luxury and bad taste are inseparable," he said. "Wherever taste is lavish it is bad. . . . Taste becomes corrupted through excessive delicacy." He also thought the simple life was more moral. He considered the dissolution of morals "the necessary consequence of luxury." His praise of country life was matched by his condemnation of city life. He said, "Men are not made to be crowded together in ant-hills, but scattered over the earth to till it. The more they are massed together, the more corrupt they become. . . . Man's breath is fatal to his fellows."

The revolution that was maturing in eighteenth-century France needed a theory of government to give legitimacy to its political goals. This theory was supplied in Rousseau's essays *On the Origin of Inequality Among Men* and *The Social Contract*. In opposition to the claim of royalty and aristocracy that they ruled by divine right and for the public good, he offered the view that they were usurpers who wielded the powers of government for their own class interests. He traced the origin of the state to the rise of the institution of private property. No government existed, he said, when men lived as savages, in the "state of nature," earning their subsistence by hunting and fishing. Each man then was free, and his own wishes were his law. But agriculture led to private property. "The cultivation of the earth necessarily brought about its distribution." The institution of property led to inequality of wealth, usurpations by the rich, and robbery by the poor. "The new born state of society," he concluded, "thus gave rise to a horrible state of war." It became necessary to create the institution of government as a means of maintaining order and, especially, of protecting the privileges of the rich. He thought this was the most natural explanation of the origin of government "because, as the poor had nothing but their freedom to lose, it would have been in the highest degree absurd for them to resign voluntarily the only good they still enjoyed, without getting anything in exchange; whereas the rich having feelings, if I may so express myself, in every part of their possessions, it was much easier to harm them, and therefore more necessary for them to take precautions against it; and, in short, because it is more reasonable to suppose a thing to have been invented by those to whom it would be of service, than by those whom it must have harmed." The rich man, however, did not frankly proclaim his motives of self-interest. Rousseau pictures him as calling to the poor, "Let us join to guard the weak from oppression." In this way he cleverly contrived to "employ in his favor the forces of those who attacked him, to make allies of his adversaries, to inspire them with different maxims, and to give them other institutions as favorable to himself as the law of nature was unfavorable." Then, says Rousseau, "all ran headlong to their chains, in hopes of securing their liberty."

In contrast to this picture of the state as it was, Rousseau offered his view of government as it ought to be. ". . . Force does not create right," he said, "and . . . we are obliged to obey only legitimate powers." The legitimate powers of government are derived from the social contract by which "each of us puts his person and all his power in common under the supreme direction of the general will." The government is set up as an instrument of the general will, but sovereignty continues to reside in the people. Considering possible forms of government, he listed three types of aristocracy: the natural, elective, and hereditary. "Natural aristocracy," in which the man most skilled in battle emerges as the tribal chief, is only for simple peoples. He rejected "hereditary aristocracy" as "the worst of all governments." The best form, he thought, was "elective aristocracy," which we know today as republican government. He believed that "the legislative power belongs to the people, and can belong to it alone." He advocated a separation of the legislative and executive powers of government. "It is not good," he said, "for him who makes the laws to execute them."

In Rousseau's theory of government, the people are sovereign, and the state should serve as an instrument of the people for carrying out the general will. But he saw that it is possible for the state to try to substitute itself for the general will, and usurp the sovereignty. In such a situation, he said, "the moment the government usurps the sovereignty, the social compact is broken, and all private citizens recover by right their natural liberty, and are forced, but not bound, to obey." Under these circumstances, he said, the people have the right to revolt. "The popular insurrection," he asserted, "that ends in the death or deposition of a Sultan is as lawful an act as those by which he disposed, the day before, of the lives and fortunes of his subjects. As he was maintained by force alone, it is force alone that overthrows him." While he wrote about the "Sultan" in *The Origin of Inequality,* he had another monarch in mind. In *Emile* he warned that "the crisis is approaching, and we are on the edge of a revolution."

Rousseau did not think that the republican form of government by itself gave assurance of equality under the law. "The universal spirit of the laws of every country," he said, "is always to take the part of the strong against the weak, and the part of him who has against him who has not; this defect is inevitable, and there is no exception to it." Equality under the law can become real equality of treatment, he believed, only when it rests on a foundation of economic equality. ". . . Laws are always of use to those who possess and harmful to those who have nothing: from which it follows that the social state is advantageous to men only when all have something and none too much." In this view, widespread ownership of the land was indispensable as the economic side of political democracy.

The Form of Rousseau's Ideas

When we examine Rousseau's ideas today, we have the advantage of hindsight. Viewing his ideas in historical perspective, we can see their connection with the social forces of his time. We can see that he was a spokesman of the lower classes struggling against the aristocracy. When he advocated widespread ownership of the land by independent farmers, he was proposing that the feudal social order be replaced by a bourgeois social order. When he argued for democratic forms of government, he was proposing the transfer of political power from the landed nobility to the common people. When he suggested that the education of boys include strong emphasis on natural science, manual training, and vocational preparation for a skilled craft, he was expressing the needs of the common people engaged in productive activity. When he glorified individualism, demanded freedom of thought, and praised simplicity of taste, he was identifying himself with the values of the new social order that was struggling against the old. But this is not the way things appeared to Rousseau. In his view, he was not trying to replace one social order by another. He was asking that the "social" order be replaced by the "natural" order. He attributed to nature the social relations that he favored. In this way he gave them the force and inevitability of natural law. He repudiated as "social"—in the sense of man-made, artificial, and unnatural—the social relations that he opposed. In this way he emphasized that they are not permanent. He attributed to the natural man all the traits of character that he considered worthy. He considered the traits that he found unworthy to be artificial products of civilization. As a result, there was a contradiction between the content of Rousseau's ideas and the form in which they were expressed. The content was the struggle of a rising social class for a new social order. But it appeared in the guise of a struggle of "nature" against "society," a struggle of "natural man" against artificial convention.

The concept of the "natural man" was a characteristic product of eighteenth-century thought. Many writers in the field of economic and political theory assumed that before men became members of society they existed in a "state of nature" as free, isolated, independent individuals living by hunting and fishing. This assumption is refuted by all the evidence of history, anthropology, and archeology. At no time in the past was man ever the free, isolated, independent individual pictured in the postulate of the "natural" man. Man from earliest times was "social" man, born into a definite social structure, dependent on his fellows, and molded in his development by the social relations within which he grew up. This is as true of the hunters of the Old Stone Age as it is of men in any other stage of social evolution. In fact, the farther back we go into the past, the more we find the individual to be submerged in his social group. But a new state of affairs took shape with the growth of production and commerce during the sixteenth, seventeenth and eighteenth centuries.

Feudal ties were dissolving. The new relations of men that were emerging were the relations of free competition in the market. In this new order, men were still, as before, connected by many threads to their fellows, but they had the appearance of independent, self-acting agents motivated by self-interest. The image of the natural man was an idealization of this man of the new order. Instead of being the starting point of history, he was actually the product of a long period of historical development. The eighteenth-century thinkers were projecting into the past an image drawn from their own time.

Rousseau perceived this mechanism of projection in the thinking of his contemporaries. "The philosophers," he said, "who have inquired into the foundations of society have all felt the necessity of going back to a state of nature; but not one of them has got there. . . . Every one of them, in short, constantly dwelling on wants, avidity, oppression, desires, and pride, has transferred to the state of nature ideas which were acquired in society; so that, in speaking of the savage, they described the social man." He also saw that the "natural law" which they claimed to describe was only the set of relations they thought desirable. "Modern writers," he said, "begin by inquiring what rules it would be expedient for men to agree on for their common interest, and then give the name of natural law to a collection of these rules, without any other proof than the good that would result from their being universally practiced." He was so well aware of the illusory character of the "state of nature" that he referred to it as "a state which no longer exists, perhaps never did exist, and probably never will exist." He confessed that his own speculations about the state of nature "must not be considered as historical truths, but only as mere conditional and hypothetical reasonings, rather calculated to explain the nature of things, than to ascertain their actual origin." Nevertheless, he took over from his contemporaries the concept of the natural man and, with it, all the inconsistencies and errors that flowed from it.

The contradication between the content of Rousseau's ideas and the form in which they were expressed is the key to understanding his many inconsistencies. Rousseau is inconsistent when he criticizes society as the source of all the evils afflicting mankind, yet merely advocates a new form of society instead of the dissolution of society. But the details of his criticism show that he is not criticizing society in general. When he speaks of "society" he means feudal society with its class stratification. In contrast, he speaks of the new order as the "natural order."

Rousseau is inconsistent when he criticizes the arts and sciences as sources of corruption, yet envisages the continued practice of the arts and sciences in the new order. But the details of his criticism show that he is not criticizing the arts and sciences in general. The target of his criticism is art and science in the service of the aristocracy. He condemns a culture that "flings garlands of flowers over the chains" that weigh men down. He castigates a decadent culture in which taste is corrupted by luxury and "excessive delicacy." He rejects the cultural standards under which "the question is no longer whether a man is honest, but whether he is clever. We do not ask whether a book is useful, but whether it is well written." In contrast, he advocates a new culture derived from "nature." In this new culture, science is an instrument of the productive classes, and works of art serve a constructive purpose; nature is the model of beauty, and "natural" simplicity is the basis of good taste.

Rousseau is inconsistent when he says that Emile cannot understand social relations until he matures sexually, yet proceeds to introduce him before puberty to the social relations of the workshop and the market place. But in Rousseau's terminology, the workshop and the market place are aspects of the "natural" order, not the "social" order. He therefore brings them into that stage of Emile's education in which he deals with "things" but not with moral principles.

Form Becomes Content

The form in which Rousseau expressed his ideas is not only a matter of terminology. The form affected the content of the ideas in a particularly significant way. When Rousseau made a sharp distinction between the "natural" order and the "social" order, between "natural" man and "social" man, he injected into the content of his ideas a definite conception of human nature. His educational views were influenced as much by this conception of human nature as by the democratic content of his social views. The consequences of this influence have persisted to the present day.

Rousseau assumed that there is an unspoiled human nature —basically good—which the child has in common with the untutored savage. This original human nature is striving for expression, he believed, and education consists of allowing it to develop in the growth of the child. A first consequence of this view was his emphasis on the importance of knowing the child. It is not necessary to agree with Rousseau's philosophy of education to recognize this emphasis as a positive contribution to education. The teacher is a craftsman working with very complicated materials. The most important and the most complicated of these materials is the child. We can teach more effectively as we learn more about how the child grows, how he learns, how he acts, and how his personality and character take shape. The study of psychology is indispensable in the professional preparation of teachers.

But Rousseau's assumption had other consequences too, and not all of them have been good. In Rousseau's view, to discover the real nature of man you must first strip him of all his social relations, of all the influences of society. The result is a human nature that is independent of society, independent of social evolution, and therefore, during the relatively short period of human history, unchanging. With all social influences excluded from the concept of human nature, all that is left is biology. Rousseau's theory therefore leads to biological determinism, the view that human behavior follows fixed patterns that are the outcomes of inherited biological drives or instincts. This view is rejected by modern anthropology, which finds that human nature is inseparable from social life; that human nature changes as society evolves; that human culture is intrinsic to human nature; that in men the instinctive basis of behavior is general and vague, and can be transformed into specific behavior patterns only through learning.

Rousseau thought of education as the cultivation of the original hereditary nature of the child. The analogy of the cultivation of plants led him to the concept of education as a process of growth. This concept has some positive merit. It emphasizes the fact that the child is an organism that is developing; that its development is a complex of dynamic processes; that education is effective only to the extent that it influences these processes. Not all the ingredients of the soil and air in which a plant grows are of value in aiding its growth. The plant selects foods according to its nature, absorbs them, and builds them into its living body. In the same way, only those parts of a child's environment enter into his education that are actively worked over by the child and are internalized, so that they become part of his makeup and share in his future activity. While this aspect of Rousseau's concept is true and beneficial, there is a side to his view that is false and harmful. Rousseau thought of growth as spontaneous growth, as an unfolding from within of inherent powers of development. But human growth is not merely an unfolding from within. Human growth involves learning. By selecting the conditions and the materials of the learning process, by choosing the experiences of the child, we can influence the outcomes of learning. Therefore the growth of children must be understood as directed growth. The theory of spontaneous growth leads to a negative, passive role for the parent and teacher. Their chief function becomes the removal of restraints that hamper the "free" development of the child's powers. But this is an abdication of responsibility by the parent and teacher. When we do not actively direct the child's development, it is directed nevertheless. It is directed by the influence of his brothers and sisters, his classmates, his friends, by the things he sees and hears and reads. It is directed by all the relationships of which he is a part and by all the activities in which he participates. If we do not have a hand in selecting them, there is no assurance that the influence will be good and that the direction of growth will be desirable.

The theory of spontaneous growth is so obviously false that it has rarely been followed with consistency. In recent times, only a few private "experimental" schools toyed with the idea, with disastrous results. Even Rousseau contradicted his own theory when he said that the teacher will choose what to teach and when to teach it, and will anticipate the child's every thought, word, and act. There are schools that, like Rousseau, try to ride both horses. They select the curriculum and the methods and materials of teaching. At the same time they claim to be fostering the *spontaneous* growth of the child. But then the theory of spontaneous growth merely serves as a screen that obscures the school's active power of choice. The school imposes a socially determined choice of goals, a socially determined choice of experiences, a socially determined set of values, and attributes them to the spontaneous unfolding of the child's natural powers. But it is better to understand that a choice has been made, so that we may decide whether we want to accept it or change it.

When Rousseau described education as a process of growth, he called attention to the essential continuity of this process. At the same time he observed that it proceeds through discontinuities, because the child passes through several qualitatively distinct stages of growth. He concluded that the materials and methods of education have to be suited to the special characteristics of each stage. We agree, today, that a method that is appropriate for infants is not suitable for ten-year-olds, and the adolescent cannot be taught by methods that are appropriate for a young child. To the extent that we recognize the existence of different levels of learning, we acknowledge a debt to Rousseau. But here, too, Rousseau's influence has not been all good. Because Rousseau thought of growth as a spontaneous development from within, he attached a narrow, specialized meaning to the stages of growth. He saw them as biologically determined, originating in changes that automatically follow each other as the organs of the body mature in accordance with a built-in physiological timetable. A consequence of this view is the tendency to *wait* for the child to progress from one stage to another. But this is not correct. A child does not spontaneously grow into a higher stage of learning. He is *prepared* for it by the learning that takes place at the lower stages. In the teaching of reading, for example, we should not *wait* until the child is ready to learn how to read. We should actively *prepare* him for reading by giving him those experiences that will help make him ready.

Rousseau performed a service to education when he emphasized the importance of arousing the child's interest. No matter how well thought out a lesson may be in other respects, it loses in effectiveness if it doesn't enlist the willing participation of the pupil. It is not enough to know *what* to teach; it is necessary to know *how* to teach it. We cannot merely pour a lesson into a pupil; we have to bring the pupil into the lesson. The problem of motivation, of making contact with the child's interests, of stirring his desire to learn, is one of the chief problems of teaching method.

Rousseau's theory of basing learning on interest, however, went far beyond the question of *methods* of teaching. It proposed a criterion for choosing the *content* of education. Because he believed that education should give free rein to the "natural" forces developing within the child, he said, "Teach the child what is of use to a child." Children "will only learn what they perceive to be of real and present value." Here is the beginning of the modern theory that education should be based on the "felt needs" of the child. The "felt needs" theory has had a strong appeal to teachers and parents, because it has the appearance of a serious attempt to fit education to the child. But under the cover of its psychological phraseology are hidden several serious errors. First, it hopelessly confuses method and content. While the child's felt needs will influence *how* we teach him, they cannot determine *what* we teach him. The source of the *content* of education is the cultural heritage of the human race. When we decide what to teach, we must take into account humanity's past and future as well as the child's present. Secondly, the theory assumes that the child's felt needs arise exclusively from within. But, actually, his felt needs reflect the influences that surround him. These may be the retarding influences of a low standard of living, the vulgarizing influences of commercialism in the movies, radio, and television, or the warping influences of ignorance and prejudice. When education is based on felt needs, these influences determine our standards of education. As a result, we tend to perpetuate a low level of culture instead of raising it. Thirdly, while it is true that education must satisfy needs, it also has the function of *creating* needs. No child spontaneously develops the need to learn arithmetic. But the school has to arouse that need, and then proceed to meet it.

Rousseau identified himself with the values of the common people who are engaged in productive labor. He was therefore able to see the fundamental importance of labor, the manipulation of materials, and concrete experience as sources of tested knowledge. He also saw how the separation of thinking from direct experience robs it of real content and turns it into an empty shell of meaningless symbols. This, in fact, was a process he detected and detested in the thinking of the feudal ruling class. He felt that the parasitic thinkers and their thoughts were equally useless. He said, ". . . If all the kings and all the philosophers were removed they would scarcely be missed, and things would go on none the worse." This outlook is reflected in his emphasis on direct activity and concrete experience in education. It is reflected further in his condemnation of meaningless verbalism, memory without understanding, and symbols divorced from content.

But Rousseau saw everything cast in the form of a conflict between "nature" and "society." This gave his ideas about the relationship between theory and practice a special twist. He regarded practice, activity, the manipulation of concrete objects as "natural." He regarded theory, thought, the use of words and symbols as artificial. So, instead of merely condemning the *isolation* of theory from practice, the *divorce* of thought from action, the *separation* of symbols from their meaning, he tended to condemn theory, thought, and symbols as such. He would not "hurry" the child into speech. He would delay teaching him to read as long as possible. He would "keep his mind idle" as long as possible. In fact, he went so far as to say that "a state of reflection is a state contrary to nature, and . . . a thinking man is a depraved animal." His emphasis on concrete activity was strongly colored by anti-intellectualism.

It is important to understand Rousseau's anti-intellectualism, because the same forces that injected it into his thinking generated a strong current of anti-intellectualism in the United States. During the early part of the nineteenth century, agrarian democracy in the United States was engaged in a struggle against the wealthy merchants and planters of the East. Hostility to upper-class privilege was easily transformed into hostility to activities that were typical of the upper class. Since the wealthy classes had a virtual monopoly of "book-learning," book-learning became an object of contempt. This latent anti-intellectualism was later reinforced by a new current generated by the growth of industry and commerce. It was strengthened and transformed by the vulgar practicality that measures the worth of all things in "cash value."

Rousseau's emphasis on concrete experience in education has been a positive influence. His anti-intellectualism has been a harmful one. Experience with concrete materials has to be the foundation of learning, but it cannot be all of learning. Our knowledge is not limited to perceptions acquired empirically. It is organized and given depth by concepts created by the human mind. We learn not only from our own experience but from the experience of others. The experience of others is transmitted through the symbols of language. Instead of delaying speech and reading and keeping the child's mind idle, we should look for ways of developing early competence in reading, and mastery of mathematics, the language of science. Symbols should not be severed from their roots in concrete experience. But symbols, the tools of thought, must not be neglected, either.

Rousseau combined his emphasis on concrete experience with a plea for the development of independent, critical thinking. He argued that the child should be allowed to make his own discoveries and draw his own conclusions. The emphasis on critical thinking was a necessary accompaniment to Rousseau's hostility to autocracy and its rule through arbitrary authority. It is still appropriate for our time, when the pressure for conformity threatens to destroy freedom of thought, the lifeblood of democracy.

But while we accept the goal of developing independent, critical thinking, we should understand the limitations on concrete activity as a means of attaining it. It sounds good to say that the child should discover everything for himself. But it is impossible. It is not possible for the child to discover by himself in a few years of "experience" what all of humanity, including its best minds, have discovered through thousands of years of experience. We must make a distinction between discovery and verification. The child will be able to discover some facts and relations for himself. There are others that he will not discover, but will be able to verify. But there are some propositions that he will neither discover nor verify by direct observation. To judge their validity he will have to be able to analyze their logic or lack of it. He will have to be able to judge their coherence and their consistency with the rest of his knowledge and experience. He will have to learn how to evaluate sources of information and judge claims of authority. To be able to do these things, he will have to have more than the experience of concrete activity. He will have to have the habit of reflective thinking, which Rousseau thought was contrary to the state of nature.

Rousseau pictured Emile as being brought up in isolation from society. His isolation was supposed to shield him from the corrupting influences of city life. Then, after his character had been formed in the country, he would enter society and help to change it for the better. Here Rousseau was giving expression to a commonly held view that the quality of a society is the product of the quality of the individuals in it. He expressed this view explicitly when he said that "to judge of men we must study the individual man," and "he who had a perfect knowledge of the inclinations of each individual might foresee all their combined effects in the body of the nation." But, actually, the opposite proposition is closer to the truth. To judge of the individual man, we must study the society of which he is a part. A man's personality and character are molded by the social relations within which he is brought up. Most educational theorists accept Rousseau's premise, and conclude that the way to improve society is to improve the individual through education. But the school does not stand apart from the forces that are operating in society. The school is not an independent force that can give direction to social development. The school is a part of society. It is run by people who grew up in society and who bring into the school all the conflicting pressures and clashing values that are generated by society. Instead of education's determining the character of society, society determines the character of education.

Rousseau did not ignore the influence of society on the individual. He saw how it presses in on him from all sides and is reflected in his every act. In fact, he recognized in the pressures of society the source of conflicts within the individual. This is a significant idea that has served as the starting point for psychologists in their attempts to understand the dynamics of personality and character development. However, Rousseau cast this idea in the form that is characteristic of all his thought. He described the conflicts within the individual as the outcome of a conflict between "nature" and "society," between "natural" feelings and the demands of "social" life. We can see the error of Rousseau's formulation when we understand that the "nature" of which he spoke was itself a social product, characteristic of his time. The conflicts within the individual reflect conflicts within the society of which he is a part. Rousseau's error persists today in schools of psychology that try to explain personality development entirely as the outcome of a conflict between biologically determined instinctive drives and socially determined restraints.

We are now in a position to make a general estimate of Rousseau's social and educational theories. The thought of Rousseau is part of the great cultural heritage of the human race. It was a step forward in man's advance toward a better life through a better understanding of the world and of himself. Rousseau made many positive contributions that we should value highly. These include his democratic criticism of feudal society; his emphasis on popular sovereignty; his perception of the relation between economic equality and political democracy; his rejection of original sin; his humane approach to children; his stress on knowing the child; his recognition of qualitatively distinct stages in the development of the child; his stress on arousing and using the child's interest; his emphasis on self-activity and concrete experience as the basis of learning; and his emphasis on the cultivation of independent, critical thinking. At the same time, we find in his ideas the source of certain errors that persist to the present day. These include the notion of growth as spontaneous growth; biological determinism in human development; the idea that the stages in the development of a child are biological in origin; the anti-intellectual depreciation of the value of thought; the underrating of knowledge that is not acquired by first-hand direct experience; the fallacy that education will change society by changing the individual; and the theory that conflicts within the individual and in society arise from a conflict between nature and society.

Suggested Readings for Chapter 1

Adler, Irving, *What We Want of Our Schools* (Chapters II and VII).
New York, The John Day Company.

Rousseau, Jean Jacques, *Emile*. New York, E. P. Dutton & Co.

———, *Social Contract and Discourses*. New York, E. P. Dutton &
Co.

2.] Mental Growth and the Art of Teaching

How should teachers teach? Before we can answer this question we must first answer another: How do pupils learn? The art of teaching, if it is to be effective, must be based on an adequate theory of learning.

There have been many different theories of learning, each having different implications for the practice of teaching. These theories may be classified according to their views of the relation between the child and his environment. One type of theory, which saw the environment as the primary active factor, was the basis of the traditional subject-centered school. A second type of theory, which saw the child as the primary active factor, led to the child-centered school. A third type of theory, which recognizes that both the child and his environment play an active role in the learning process, is the foundation for contemporary teaching.

The first type of theory was not always explicitly formulated. But it could easily be recognized as being implicit in school practices which cast the teacher in the role of someone who literally gives the child an education, and cast the child in the role of someone who passively receives it. Various metaphors have been used to describe the theories of this type: The child is a receptacle into which knowledge can be poured; the child's mind is a *tabula rasa* on which the teacher can write at will; the child's mind is like clay, to be molded into a socially desirable form.

Theories of this type have been rejected in favor of a different view that underlies the theories of the second and third types. In this view the child is a self-acting organism that grows. Learning is not a mere accumulation of knowledge, but is a process of growth. This view has led to the emergence of developmental theories of psychology, including some theories of mental growth.

Theories of learning of the first type had pictured the environment as active, and the child as relatively passive. The first critics of these theories, reacting against them, went to the other extreme and formulated theories of the second type, which pictured the child as active and the environment as relatively passive. These theories of the second type, direct descendants of the educational philosophy of Rousseau, have already been discussed in Chapter 1. However, since these theories have influenced contemporary teaching in many ways, both good and bad, it will be worthwhile to summarize and evaluate here again some of their principal features.

A composite model of some typical theories of the second type would include propositions like these: Before we can educate the child, we must study the child to find out his nature and needs. The child is growing, and his growth is to be understood as an unfolding from within. The function of the school is to supply growth-promoting nutrients, as soil does to a growing plant. The child learns only through his own activity. This activity should be directed by the child's needs of the moment, and not by any adult purpose.

The child learns nothing from words that are divorced from meaning. So verbal learning should be avoided. The growth of the child takes him through several qualitatively distinct stages of development. Instruction during any particular stage should be tailored to what the child needs and is ready for at that stage. If he is not yet ready for a particular type of learning experience, it is necessary to wait until he becomes ready through spontaneous maturation.

When these propositions are subjected to critical analysis and the test of experience, we find that some of them are true and help to guide us toward good teaching practices, while others are false and serve as obstacles to good teaching. It is true that we should study the child we must teach, and recognize that he is growing. It is not true that his growth is a process of unfolding from within. An important aspect of his growth is his assimilation of part of the cultural heritage of his generation. His growth is not spontaneous growth. It is directed growth, and the teacher plays an important part in giving it direction. It is true that words divorced from meaning are useless, but it is not true that all verbal learning is useless. In fact, it is chiefly through verbal learning that the child gains access to the knowledge that mankind has accumulated through thousands of years. It is true that we should not teach the child what he is not ready for. But it is not true that we should wait until he is ready. Instead of waiting passively, we should actively help him to become ready.

The principal errors of the theories of the second type are avoided in the recent theories of the third type, which recognize the active role of both the pupil and his environment in the learning process. One of these newer theories is the developmental psychology of Jean Piaget. Since it is based in part on studies of how the child develops his conceptions of number and space, this theory is of particular importance to mathematics teachers and is the subject of the rest of this chapter.

Piaget's theory of mental growth is based on observations he and his co-workers have made in a series of experiments in which children of various ages were confronted with problems to solve and tasks to learn. Because of flaws in his experimental technique, which we need not discuss here, it is not possible to say that his theory has been conclusively proved. However, a brilliant flash of insight, unproved by the evidence offered for it, may nevertheless be right. And even if it is not fully right, it may be illuminating. Piaget's thought is full of such brilliant flashes of insight. Keeping in mind that his ideas are to be considered suggestive rather than conclusive, let us examine his theory of mental growth and its implications for the art of teaching.

Everybody is talking about Piaget, but not many people are reading him. His views are widely misinterpreted and misunderstood. So it is necessary to summarize them with particular care. The summary that I present here lists twelve significant features.

1. Piaget asserts that the basis of all learning is the child's own activity as he interacts with his physical and social environment.

2. The child's mental activity is organized into structures. Separate mental acts are related to each other and grouped together in clusters called "schemas" or patterns of behavior.

3. Mental activity, like metabolic activity, is a process of *adaptation* to the environment. Adaptation consists of two opposed but inseparable processes, *assimilation* and *accom-*

modation. Assimilation is the process whereby the child fits every new experience into his preexisting mental structures. Through the functioning of these structures, he interprets his new experiences in the light of his old experiences. The process of assimilation is a kind of inertia of mental structures, a tendency of these structures to persist. However, the incorporation of new experiences into old structures inevitably modifies them. Accommodation is the process of perpetual modification of mental structures to meet the requirements of each particular experience. Accommodation is the tendency of mental structures to change under the influence of the environment.

4. Mental growth is a social process. The child does not interact with his physical environment as an isolated individual. He interacts with it as part of a social group. Consequently his social environment mediates between him and his physical environment. His interaction with other people plays an important part in the development of the child's view of the world. It is only through an exchange of ideas with other people that he becomes aware of the one-sided subjective character of his own point of view. It is only by combining the viewpoints of others with his own that he evolves from a subjective to an objective outlook.

5. Although accommodation to the environment leads to a continuous modification of the child's schemas or behavior patterns, the change is not merely quantitative. In the course of time the child's mental structures undergo qualitative changes as well. As the child progresses from infancy to maturity, his characteristic ways of acting and thinking are changed several times as new mental structures emerge out of the old ones modified by accumulated accommodations. Piaget finds that the child passes through four distinct stages

of mental growth, which he calls the *sensori-motor stage,* the *pre-operational stage,* the stage of *concrete operations,* and the stage of *formal operations.*

The child is in the sensori-motor stage from birth to the age of about eighteen months. During this stage, the child's inherited reflexes are gradually modified by experience and combined into complex patterns of behavior. His activity becomes less body-centered and more object-centered. He becomes aware of the relationship between means and ends in the manipulation of objects. Finally, he becomes aware of the fact that objects exist even when he does not perceive them. Once he has developed the concept of separately existing objects, he is capable of thinking of an object that he does not see. He is then able to plan an action mentally before he carries it out physically. This marks the transition to the next stage of development, the pre-operational stage, in which sensori-motor activity is accompanied by mental activity based on the mental representation of objects and mental anticipations of activities.

The child is in the pre-operational stage from the age of eighteen months to the age of six or seven years. During this stage, the child has already begun to use symbols. They are private symbols at first, and then, as he learns to speak, they are the socially standardized symbols of spoken language. He is egocentric in his view of objects and events. That is, he is incapable of seeing things from any but his own point of view. His thinking is dominated by what he sees at the moment. In his examination of a situation involving several factors that operate at the same time, he tends to fix attention on one factor to the exclusion of the others. In examining a change from one state to another, he fixes his attention on the initial and the final states and ignores the transformation that produced the change. As a result, he is not aware that when two changes occur simultaneously, one may compensate for the other. For example, if a ball of clay is rolled into a sausage shape, its length increases, but its width decreases. The pre-operational child, fixing his attention on the increase in length, will conclude that the sausage has more clay than the original ball because it is longer. He does not see that the decrease in width has compensated for the increase in length. He is not yet aware that the mass of a body is conserved when it is subjected to changes of form or dimension. Similarly, he is not yet aware of the fact that the cardinal number of a set is independent of the arrangement of its members. Since a set of five blocks arranged in a line with spaces between adjacent blocks makes a longer line than the same blocks arranged with no spaces between them, he thinks that the first arrangement has more blocks than the second.

Because of his tendency to fix attention on only one factor at a time, he often comes to contradictory conclusions as he shifts his attention from one factor to another. He will assert the contradictory conclusions without any concern for their inconsistency. Because he tends to neglect transformations from one state to another, he is not aware of the reversibility of many transformations. Because his thinking is dominated by his momentary perception, he tends to associate things with each other by accidents of juxtaposition rather than by any relation of cause and effect or of logical implication. As a result he has a poor grasp of the relation between part and whole, between element and set, or between subset and set.

The child is in the stage of concrete operations between the ages of seven and eleven. In this stage he has already separated the concept of mass from the concept of length, and the concept of cardinal number from the concept of end-to-end length. He knows that the mass of an object remains unchanged when its form is changed, and he knows that the cardinal number of a set remains unchanged when the arrangement of the set is altered. He has mastered the relationship between set and subset so that he can form hierarchies of sets that are related by inclusion. He has grasped the transitive property of order relations, so that he is able to form ordered sets and establish order-preserving one-to-one correspondences.

The words "operations" and "concrete" that Piaget uses to name this stage symbolize the features that distinguish this stage from those that precede and follow it. The operations that Piaget is talking about are mental acts. Piaget defines an operation as "an action which can return to its starting point, and which can be integrated with other actions also possessing this feature of reversibility." For example, rolling a ball of clay into a sausage shape is an operation as well as a physical act if the child is aware of it as only one of many changes of form that may be imposed in sequence on the lump of clay, and if he is aware that every such change of form can be reversed or undone. This awareness that actions are reversible and may be combined with other actions makes operational thinking more flexible and more penetrating than pre-operational thinking. Because operations are reversible and can be combined, a system of operations has the structure of a mathematical group, with a law of composition of elements, an identity element, an inverse for every element, and an associative law. (See the definition of a group on page 160.) The child makes the transition from the pre-operational stage to the stage of concrete operations when his mental acts that used to be isolated and unrelated are finally organized into such grouplike structures.

Piaget calls the mental operations of the child between seven and eleven "concrete" operations because the starting point for them is always some real system of objects and relations that he perceives. The child in this stage can organize and order only what is immediately present for him. He makes the transition to the next higher stage of thinking ability, the stage of formal operations, when he begins to reason about things that he does not see, when he can reason about the potential as well as the real.

The stage of formal operations, which the child enters at about the age of eleven or twelve, is the stage of adult reasoning. In this stage, the child can identify all the possible factors that are relevant to a problem under investigation. He can use combinatorial analysis to form all possible combinations of these factors, one at a time, two at a time, three at a time, and so on. He can formulate hypotheses, draw conclusions from them, and test them against reality. Moreover, he can explore the relations of propositions, not only the relations of things. In short, he is capable of scientific thinking and formal mathematical reasoning. Since formal reasoning involves propositions about propositions, or, in Piaget's terminology, operations on operations, Piaget sometimes refers to formal operations as *operations to the second power.*

6. According to Piaget, perception is not the mere passive registering of raw sensation by the child's sense organs. It is to be understood as *perceptual activity,* in which the child's brain organizes the sensations he gathers in the course of his exploratory activity. His perception of space, for example, is compounded out of images formed on the retina of the eye, the kinesthetic sensations of moving and focusing the eyes, and the coordination of hand and eye in reaching for things,

grasping them, moving them, arranging them, and so on. The child's ability to perceive, like his ability to think, undergoes development with age.

7. There is a time lag between the development of a child's ability to perceive a thing and the development of his ability to form a mental image of that thing when it is not perceptually present.

8. In the development of the child's concepts of space, topological notions, such as proximity, separation, order, enclosure, and continuity, arise first. Projective and Euclidean notions arise later.*

9. In the development of the child's concept of number, his grasp of order relations and cardinal number grow hand in hand.

10. As the child advances from infancy to maturity, his thinking evolves from a short-range, static, egocentric outlook to a long-range, dynamic coordination of many points of view. This evolution is punctuated by the emergence of a succession of concepts of *invariance:* first the concept of the permanence of the object; then the concepts of the invariance of mass, volume, weight, etc.

11. The order in which a child progresses through the four major stages of mental growth is fixed. But his rate of progress is not fixed. The transition from one stage to the next can be hastened by enriched experience and good teaching. Piaget expresses this idea in these words in his book *The Growth of Logical Thinking from Childhood to Adoles-*

---

* This view seems to be contradicted by recent experiments of T. G. R. Bower. Bower's experiments show that infants between six and eight weeks old can recognize the size and shape of an object (Euclidean properties) even when the retinal image of the object is varied by varying the distance and orientation of the object. ("The Visual World of Infants," *Scientific American,* December 1966).

cence: ". . . the maturation of the nervous system can do no more than determine the totality of possibilities and impossibilities at a given stage. A particular social environment remains indispensable for the realization of these possibilities. It follows that their realization can be accelerated or retarded as a function of cultural and educational conditions."

12. Piaget constructed elaborate mathematical models of the mental structures that are characteristic of the stages of concrete operations and formal operations. Since his mathematical models shed little light on the art of teaching, I shall give no details about them.

As you can see even from this sketchy outline, Piaget's theory of mental growth contains many subtleties and complexities. Actually, the theory is so complex that any abbreviated version cannot do it justice. Some of the short accounts of the theory that have been prepared for popular consumption eliminate the subtleties and complexities, and thus oversimplify the theory and leave it open to misinterpretation. This is true even of the article that Piaget himself had written for the November 1953 issue of *Scientific American*. Because of the wide currency of these abbreviated accounts of the theory, some gross errors have been made in interpreting and applying it. Two errors in particular have had a great influence.

The first of these errors is made by people who interpret Piaget's theory to mean that the stages in a child's mental growth are correlated exclusively with chronological age. On the basis of this interpretation, they conclude that the school cannot hasten the child's progress from one stage to the next, that it must wait for him to mature spontaneously, and that, meanwhile, the best it can do is supply the child with experiences that he is able to assimilate into the mental structure that he has at the moment. Now it is true that Piaget studied only the relationship between mental growth and chronological age. He did not choose to examine the influence of other factors, such as socio-economic status, methods of teaching, individual differences, and so on. But this does not mean that the other factors have no influence. In fact, Piaget himself has said that there are three factors that play a part in preparing the child to advance from one stage of mental growth to the next. These are "maturation of the nervous system, experience acquired in interaction with the physical environment, and the influence of the social milieu." Moreover, Piaget's theory stresses that while an experience is assimilated into the child's mental structure, the structure is at the same time accommodated to the experience, so that it is changed by the experience. The people who fix their attention on only the maturation factor in growth, or only on the assimilation factor in adaptation, and ignore the other factors, are behaving like the child who fixes his attention on only the change in the length of a piece of rolled clay while he ignores the change in its width. That is, they are in the pre-operational stage in their thinking about mental growth.

The second major error in interpreting Piaget is made by people who emphasize exclusively the child's self-activity in the learning process. These are the enthusiasts for the so-called discovery method of teaching, who insist that the child must always be allowed to make his own discoveries without any help from his peers or from his teacher. Now it is true that we should provide every possible opportunity for the child to make through his own efforts discoveries that are within his reach. But it is also true that there are many discoveries that are beyond his reach. There are many facts and relationships that a child can be led to understand even though he cannot discover them himself. There are some discoveries that he *can* make, if he is guided to them by carefully selected experiences and skillfully formulated questions. Moreover, as Piaget has stressed, the exchange of ideas between a child and his classmates is an important learning experience that should not be sacrificed while we pursue the mirage of each child making all his discoveries by himself in splendid isolation.

If we reject these two errors, it does not mean that we reject any attempt to seek guidance from Piaget's theory for the improvement of the curriculum and methods of teaching. These errors have arisen not from using Piaget's theory but from abusing it. Piaget's theory, properly understood, does have many fruitful implications for the art of teaching. I list a baker's dozen of them in the paragraphs that follow. Because of limitations of space, I must describe each of these implications in only a few words. However, exploring all the ramifications of each could easily take many pages of discussion. An adequate treatment of the implications of Piaget's theory of mental growth for the teaching of mathematics would require at least a full-length book.

Here, then, are some of the implications, as I see them.

1. Since the child's mental growth advances through qualitatively distinct stages, these stages should be taken into account when we plan the curriculum. We should use two criteria for selecting the mathematical experiences a child should have at any given age: (*a*) they should be experiences that he is ready for, in view of the stage of mental growth that the child has reached; (*b*) they should help prepare the

child to advance to the next stage. We should not teach a topic too early, but we should also not delay for years a topic that he is ready for. For example, in the traditional mathematics curriculum, the child had little experience with deductive reasoning from hypotheses until he studied geometry at the age of fifteen. However, Piaget's studies show that the child enters the stage of formal operations, the stage of deductive reasoning from hypotheses, at the age of eleven or twelve. It is therefore psychologically sound for us to introduce short units of deductive reasoning from hypotheses as early as the sixth grade. A suitable deductive unit in arithmetic, for example, is the derivation of the rule for multiplying fractions from the associative and commutative laws of multiplication and the rules for multiplying a unit fraction by a whole number or another unit fraction.*

2. Before introducing a new concept to the child, test him to be sure that he has all the prerequisites for mastering this concept. If he is not yet ready for the concept, provide him with the experiences that will help him become ready. Of course this is not a new principle. It has been well known to teachers ever since the days of Herbart.

3. The preadolescent child makes typical errors of thinking that are characteristic of his stage of mental growth. We should try to understand these errors. Piaget has given us a profile of the thought processes of the pre-operational child and the child in the stage of concrete operations. We should be thoroughly familiar with these profiles. But that is not enough. Besides knowing what errors the child usually makes, we should also try to find out why he makes them. We should keep in mind that an answer or an action that seems

* See Irving Adler, *A New Look at Arithmetic* (New York, The John Day Company), pp. 179–184.

illogical from our point of view on the basis of our extensive experience may seem perfectly logical from the child's point of view on the basis of his limited experience. Before we can get the child to understand what we are saying to him, we must first understand in his own terms and on his own ground what the child is saying to us.

For example, when a three-year-old child concludes that a lump of clay rolled into a sausage has more clay than the same lump rolled into a ball, because the sausage is longer than the ball, he is wrong. But in terms of his own limited experience, he is being logical. When he made a "train" with blocks, he observed that by using more and more blocks he could make a longer and longer train. When he ate a banana he observed that the shorter the banana became, the less banana he had left to eat. In short, he had observed a correlation between quantity of matter and length. It is true that the correlation is valid only if other factors, such as width, are kept constant. But his experience had not yet called to his attention the fact that the correlation he had observed had a restricted domain of validity. When he used the correlation to judge the amount of matter in the rolled lump of clay, he was extrapolating the correlation beyond the domain in which its validity had been tested. But it is important to keep in mind that this kind of extrapolation of a rule beyond the domain in which it has been verified is not necessarily a mistake. In fact, scientists are doing it all the time, only they call it scientific prediction. Sometimes the prediction is verified, and we know then that the rule has a broader domain of application. Sometimes the prediction is refuted, and we begin to recognize the limits of the domain in which the rule is valid. Sometimes an impermissible extrapolation leads to the discovery of new knowledge, as the impermissible extrapolation of the square-root operation to negative real numbers led to the discovery of imaginary numbers. The three-year-old is a young scientist who has learned from experience to judge mass by length. With more experience he will discover that this criterion is inadequate.

Actually the three-year-old child does not merely see mass and length as correlated. He goes beyond that and sees them as only barely distinguishable. For the pre-operational child, these two concepts, together with those of volume and cardinal number, have only begun to exist as separate concepts. At first they are all fused into a single vague concept of *amount*. These concepts are fused in the child's mind because they are fused in his experience. The single concept of amount becomes differentiated into the separate concepts of mass, volume, length and cardinal number only as the child's experience establishes the need for this differentiation.

4. We can help the child overcome the errors in his thinking by providing him with experiences that expose them as errors and point the way to the correction of the errors. For example, the pre-operational child judges the number of blocks in a line of blocks by the length of the line, without regard to the fact that empty spaces as well as blocks may be contributing to the length of the line. To overcome this error, we should have the child perform two pairs of inverse operations: the insertion and removal of spaces, and the insertion and removal of blocks. Many varied experiences of this kind will help to separate the concept of length of the line from the concept of number of blocks in the line. Also the use of these inverse physical operations will help to crystallize the inverse mental operations that are characteristic of the next stage of growth, the stage of concrete operations.

5. The child in the pre-operational stage tends to fix his

attention on one variable to the neglect of others. To help him overcome this error, provide him with many situations like the one just described in which he may explore the influences of two or more variables.

6. A child's thinking is more flexible when it is based on reversible operations. For this reason we should teach pairs of inverse operations in arithmetic together. We should teach that subtraction and addition nullify each other, and multiplication and division nullify each other.

7. The child in the stage of concrete operations has an incomplete grasp of the relations among the subsets of a set. To close the gaps in his thinking, have him explore by direct observation various sets and their subsets, unions of sets, intersections of sets, and hierarchies of inclusion of sets, as these arise naturally in the learning situation.

8. A prerequisite for the stage of formal operations is the ability to carry out simple combinatorial analysis. All combinatorial analysis is based on the formation of Cartesian products of sets. We can easily teach children systematic ways of forming these products by using tree diagrams and rectangular arrays.*

9. Mental growth is encouraged by the experience of seeing things from many different points of view. Although this is especially important for the young child, it should not be neglected in teaching the older child and the adolescent. For example, in the tenth grade we should use many different approaches to the study of geometry. We should use not only the traditional synthetic approach but also the analytic approach via coordinates, the vector approach, and the approach that is based on the use of isometries of the plane. This point is discussed more fully in Chapter 7.

* See *A New Look at Arithmetic*, pp. 10–12.

10. Physical action is one of the bases of learning. To learn effectively, the child must be a participant in events, not merely a spectator. To develop his concepts of number and space, it is not enough that he look at things. He must also touch things, move them, turn them, put them together, and take them apart. For every new concept that we want the child to acquire, we should start with some relevant action that he can perform. For example, to pave the way for the concept of an angle, we should give him opportunities to turn a hand of a clock or a pointer on a dial.

However, the child's activity should not be kept forever on the level of physical action. The physical action is merely the foundation for the mental operation that we want to develop. We should create opportunities for the child to be less and less dependent on the physical action until the action is entirely internalized as a mental operation. Thus, while we may introduce the addition of integers as a succession of motions on the number line, we should lead the child to discover as rapidly as possible ways of doing the addition mentally without recourse to the number line.

11. Since there is a lag between perception and the formation of a mental image, reinforce the developing mental image with frequent use of perceptual data. For example, any time that the child falters in the addition of integers, let him see the addition once more as a succession of motions on the number line.

12. Since mental growth is associated with the discovery of invariants, we should make more frequent use of a systematic search for those features of a situation that remain unchanged under a particular group of transformations. This is both good psychology and good mathematics. In elementary arithmetic, for example, after the equivalence of two sets has

been established by a one-to-one correspondence, have the child observe the effect of making substitutions for the elements of the sets or the effect of changing the arrangement of the elements in each set. In geometry, we should certainly make more frequent use of groups of transformations than we do.

13. Piaget claims that topological relations are the first geometric relations that are observed by the child. Whether this claim turns out to be true or false, it is certainly true that topological relations are observed *early* by the very young child. However, they are the last ones that were studied explicitly and formally by mathematicians. The reason for this paradox is that topological relations appear obvious intuitively. Because they are so obvious, the child grasps them early. Also, because they are so obvious, the mathematician tended to take them for granted in his first attempts to develop geometry as an axiomatic structure. There is a lesson for us here concerning the way in which we should deal with topological relations in the schools. We should be careful not to overdo the formalization of the study of topological relations in the tenth grade and below. Children, like the mathematicians of earlier centuries, will not see the need for trying to prove deductively relations that appear to them to be intuitively obvious.

While we take note of the implications of Piaget's theory for the art of teaching, we must also be on guard against possible confusions that may arise from a misreading of his theory. I call attention to two of these possible confusions that may arise from misunderstanding Piaget's use of the terms "concrete operations" and "formal operations."

1. Piaget's use of the word *concrete* in the term "concrete operations" should not be confused with the uses of the word in everyday speech. For Piaget, the concrete operations of a person are mental operations with propositions about some real system of objects and relations that the person perceives. What is concrete or not concrete in this sense is relative to the person's past experience and his mental maturity. To the kindergarten child, uniting a set of two beads with a set of three beads is concrete, but adding the numbers 2 and 3 is not. For the ninth-grade student, the sum $2 + 3$ is concrete, but the sum $x + y$ is not. For the student getting his first introduction to abstract algebra, the additive group of integers is concrete, but the concept of an abstract group is not.

The fact that the stage of mental growth between the ages of seven and eleven is called the stage of concrete operations does not mean that concrete operations are not used at a later age. Concrete operations are used at all stages past the age of seven, but until the age of about eleven they are, in general, the most advanced operations of which the child is capable. Moreover, in the development of new concepts at all stages of learning, it is necessary to proceed from the concrete to the abstract.

2. At the age of eleven or twelve, the child begins to be capable of formal operations, or deductive reasoning from hypotheses. This does not mean that he is incapable of deductive reasoning before then. Concrete operations include deductive reasoning. For example, when the child reasons that $4 + 2 = 4 + 1 + 1 = 5 + 1 = 6$, he is doing deductive reasoning. Opportunities for deductive reasoning should not be neglected in the elementary grades. Of course the deductive reasoning in this stage should be restricted to reasoning about real objects and relations that the child perceives.

Piaget, through his studies of child development and his theoretical activity, has produced a vast treasury of ideas on how children learn and think. The job of drawing on this treasury for the benefit of the teaching of mathematics has only just begun. I urge that this job be pursued with greater vigor on the basis of a more serious attempt to understand the subtleties and complexities of Piaget's theory.

Suggested Readings for Chapter 2

Adler, Irving, *A New Look at Arithmetic* (pages 10–12, 179–184). New York, The John Day Company.

Bower, T. G. R., "The Visual World of Infants." *Scientific American,* December 1966.

Flavell, John H., *The Developmental Psychology of Jean Piaget.* New York, D. Van Nostrand Co., Inc.

Piaget, Jean, *The Child's Conception of Number.* New York, Humanities Press.

Piaget, Jean and Inhelder, Bärbel, *The Child's Conception of Space.* New York, Humanities Press.

——, *The Growth of Logical Thinking from Childhood to Adolescence.* New York, Basic Books.

3.] The Changes Taking Place in Mathematics

THERE is now a vigorous movement under way to reexamine and modify the teaching of mathematics. The avowed purpose of this movement is to bring the teaching of mathematics up to date by taking into account the changes that have taken place in mathematics. It is necessary to begin, then, by making a survey of the nature and significance of these changes. We make such a survey in this chapter. This is not the first such survey, nor will it be the last. The improvement of instruction in mathematics is a continuing process that never ends. Those who participate in this process must keep turning their heads to look repeatedly, now at mathematics, now at the schools. I hope that by taking a new look at the new mathematics in this chapter, we may find some fresh insights into what must be done to make the teaching of mathematics more effective.

What are the distinguishing characteristics of contemporary mathematics? It seems to me that there are four of them, which I would describe as follows:

1. Contemporary mathematics is classical mathematics grown mature.

2. Contemporary mathematics is classical mathematics grown self-conscious and self-critical.

3. It is also modern mathematics, which developed as a more efficient way of dealing with the content of classical mathematics.

4. Finally, it is mathematics that is more and more intimately related to man's activities in industry, social life, science and philosophy.

We shall examine each of these four characteristics in turn.

Classical Mathematics Grown Mature

Classical mathematics may be described as the study of number and space. The study of number became arithmetic, algebra and analysis. The study of space became geometry. We shall note and comment on six aspects of the growth to maturity of classical mathematics.

Change from number system to number systems

We no longer have just one number system. We have many number systems. The pluralization of the concept of number system developed in two ways. First, there was a steady expansion of the original number system of everyday use. At first the only numbers known were the natural numbers, used for counting. The requirements of measurement led to the introduction of rational numbers. Geometric theory led to the introduction of irrational numbers. Algebraic theory led to the introduction of negative numbers and complex numbers. If we recognize as a number system any set of numbers that is closed under addition and multiplication, subject to the usual associative, commutative and distributive laws, then we see that the expansion of the number system has given us five number systems, one within the other. We have the system of natural numbers within the system of integers within the system of rational numbers within the system of real numbers within the system of complex numbers.*

Secondly, more number systems were introduced in the course of the development of arithmetic and algebra. In the first place there was a modification and elaboration of the concept of number system by the introduction of the concepts of group, ring, field, and vector space. There was also the discovery of many new structures which were like number systems in the sense that they too were groups, or rings, or fields or vector spaces. For example, the set of all permutations of n objects is a group, where permutations are "multiplied" by performing them one after the other. The set of numbers $a + b\sqrt{2}$, where a and b are rational, is a field. The set of residue classes of integers modulo an integer m is a ring. It is a field if m is a prime number. The set of all polynomials with real coefficients is a ring. If p is a prime, and q is a power of p, then the set of all roots modulo p of the equation $x^q - x = 0$ is a field. The set of n by n matrices whose terms are complex numbers is a vector space over the complex field, etc. Additional systems that were something like number systems were also discovered in other areas of study. In the study of logic an algebra of propositions was developed in which disjunction played the role of addition and conjunction played the role of multiplication. In the study of the theory of sets, an algebra of

* See Irving Adler, *The New Mathematics* (New York, The John Day Company).

subsets of a set was developed in which union played the role of addition and intersection played the role of multiplication.

An incidental but important result of the refinement and pluralization of the concept of number system was that we finally learned how to ask a question sensibly in algebra. We used to look for roots of an algebraic equation without knowing exactly what we were looking for. As a result we weren't quite sure about whether we could believe in the results we obtained. For example, some mathematicians, like Descartes, used to reject complex roots as meaningless. Now we are very specific in formulating our questions in an unambiguous manner. We specify a domain in which a problem is defined and in which an answer is sought. For example, we may say, "Given an algebraic equation with coefficients in the real field, does it have roots in the real field? Does it have roots in some extension field of the real field?"

Change from geometry to geometries

We no longer have just one geometry. We have many geometries. The pluralization of the concept of geometry developed in two separate ways. We found that there are other spaces besides the traditional three-dimensional Euclidean space. We also found that there are many geometries within any given space.

The attempts to prove the parallel postulate led to the recognition that there is a space (Lobatschewskian) that satisfies all the axioms of Euclid except the parallel postulate. Thus we got two geometric spaces, Euclidean and non-Euclidean, instead of one. Then Riemann gave us an infinite number of spaces by showing that a space can be constructed by using any one of an infinite number of quadratic forms to define a metric on a manifold. More spaces were obtained by recognizing the validity of spaces of n dimensions, where n is any positive integer.*

In the study of Euclidean space of three dimensions, many separate geometries emerged. One is the geometry of congruence and a second is the geometry of similarity. In addition there are the geometry of incidence relations (projective geometry), the geometry based on concepts of nearness and connectedness (topology), and many others such as inversion geometry and affine geometry.

Unification of the concepts of number and space

The separate disciplines of algebra and geometry converged toward each other and joined in Cartesian geometry. This resulted in a fusion of the notions of number and space. The real number system, for example, is nothing but a Euclidean line, and the complex number system is nothing but a Euclidean plane. Algebraists, of course, would prefer to say it the other way around.

Development of analysis

Various concepts and techniques that are based on the idea of *limit* were introduced into mathematics. These include such notions as continuity, the sum of an infinite series, derivative (which is a limit of a quotient), and definite integral (which is a limit of a sum). The development of analysis led to a new dichotomy in the subject matter of mathematics to replace the old one of number versus space. We recognized that the number system (real or complex) has an algebraic aspect, found in the properties of the operations addition and multiplication,

---

* See Irving Adler, *A New Look at Geometry* (New York, The John Day Company).

and a topological aspect based on the concept of nearness and which underlies all considerations of convergence. These two aspects of the number system can be studied separately or in combination.

Evolution of the concept of function

There has been a gradual development of a more and more general concept of function. The first functions employed were algebraic functions. The study of trigonometry led to the introduction of the circular functions. Calculus contributed the logarithmic function (the integral of dx/x), and its inverse, the exponential function. The pendulum problem contributed elliptic integrals and functions. The theory of heat contributed functions defined by Fourier series. Experience with many functions ultimately led to recognition of the fact that a function need not have a derivative, and does not even have to be continuous.

Development of theories of functionals

A functional is a special kind of function. Its domain is a set of subsets of a space. Its range is a set of numbers. A typical example of a functional is a line integral. Our common measures of length, area and volume are also functionals that assign a number to a set of points in Euclidean space. The study of physics introduces other functionals such as mass, electrical charge, etc.

A special branch of mathematics, the calculus of variations, deals with the problem of maximizing or minimizing the value of a functional. It tells us, for example, that a plane figure whose perimeter has a given length has the maximum possible area if its perimeter is a circle.

Classical Mathematics Grown Self-Conscious and Self-Critical

The tumultuous growth of mathematics during a period of more than 2,000 years produced a great superstructure resting on a very shaky foundation. During the second half of the nineteenth century, mathematicians undertook a systematic analysis of the foundations of mathematics in order to plug the holes that had developed. We note some of the questions that they raised and answered. The answers to these questions have helped to give contemporary mathematics its characteristic flavor.

What is a number?

Weird numbers like the square root of 2 or the square root of -1 had been introduced as a convenience. What did they really mean, and why were they legitimately called numbers? The answer to this question was supplied by what we might call "Operation Bootstrap"—the constructive definition of larger and more adequate number systems with the help of the smaller and less adequate ones. The natural numbers are used to construct the integers, the integers are used to construct the rationals, the rationals are used to construct the reals, and the reals are used to construct the complex number system. At each stage of the construction, it is proved as a theorem in the smaller system that the larger system that has been constructed really exists. This removes once and for all the mystery that lurked in the shadows of our earlier vague notions of the irrational and the imaginary.

What is a continuum?

This question had plagued mathematics since the days of Zeno and his famous paradoxes. The answer was supplied by the Dedekind-Cantor theory of irrationals. Developing this theory required excursions into the theory of point sets.

What is infinity?

The concept of infinity crept into mathematics through many doors. It entered in the form of the infinite divisibility of the Euclidean line. It also entered in the form of the infinite extensibility of the Euclidean line. It popped up again in infinite series and the definite integral. Riemann cleared up one confusion by making the distinction between unbounded and infinite. A plane and a sphere, for example, are both unbounded, but while a plane is infinite, a sphere is finite. Cantor finally brought infinity under control by developing the theory of sets and of transfinite numbers. The theory of sets had its own troubles in the form of apparent contradictions. But these were ultimately eliminated by axiomatizing the theory, and by excluding from consideration such unmanageable ideas as "the set of all sets."

What is a variable?

For quite some time mathematicians relied on the rather meaningless answer that a variable was a number that changed while it was under discussion. A better and more meaningful answer came from the further development of the science of logic: A variable is merely a dummy that may be replaced by any element of a given set. Closely related to the concept of variable is that of an open sentence. An open sentence is a sort of printing press for printing a lot of statements that have the same form. A statement is produced by the open sentence by replacing each variable in it by some element selected from a specified set.

What is a function?

In the happy days of the past, all the functions people ever had to use were represented by well-behaved analytic expressions. This led to very naïve notions of what a function is, based on the use of formulas or graphs. It was assumed that every curve defined a continuous function and that every continuous function had a derivative. But then pathological cases began to arise, such as a continuous function that had no derivative or a curve that filled a square. The concept of function was finally clarified when it was separated from the concept of curve and was defined in its most general form on the basis of the theory of sets: A function is a mapping of one set of elements into another set of elements. Or alternatively it is defined as a particular kind of subset of the Cartesian product of the domain and range. An incidental result of the perfected concept of function is that *many-valued functions* have been banished from the realm of legitimate ideas. By definition, every function is single-valued.

What is an integral?

The first integrals were integrals of continuous functions over a finite interval. It soon became necessary to extend the concept of integrability to make room for integrals of discontinuous functions, such as step functions, and for integrals over the infinite real line. Lebesgue raised the question of how far we can generalize the concept of integrability and of integral, and answered it by developing the theory of measure and the

Lebesgue integral. Underlying the theory of measure is the concept of a *measurable space* defined by means of a σ-ring of subsets of the space (a ring closed under differences and denumerable unions). Measure theory now provides a rigorous foundation for the theory of probability.

What is a geometry?

Felix Klein answered this question with the help of the concept of a group of transformations. A given space can be mapped into itself in many ways. Of particular interest are those mappings called transformations that are one to one and have the entire space as range. The set of all such transformations is a group. For each subgroup of this group it is possible to consider questions such as these: What figures in this space are mapped onto each other by the transformations of the subgroup? What properties of these figures remain unchanged when the figures are transformed? Klein proposed the fruitful idea that the study of such questions for any subgroup constitutes a geometry. Thus there is a geometry belonging to every one of these subgroups of the full transformation group. On the basis of this idea it is possible to set up hierarchies of geometries. When the group of one geometry is a subgroup of the group of another geometry, the latter geometry is more general than the former. The theorems of the geometry determined by the larger group become theorems of the geometry determined by the smaller group. For example, the geometry of similarity in Euclidean geometry belongs to a particular group of transformations of affine space. The geometry of congruences belongs to a subgroup of that group. The theorems about similar figures also apply to congruent figures. That is, congruence is a special case of similarity. One of the most beautiful results of this approach to the study of geometry was Klein's demonstration of the existence of both Euclidean geometry and non-Euclidean geometry within projective geometry.

Axiomatization of Euclidean geometry

Euclid's *Elements* undertook the task of developing geometry as a deductive system, in which all theorems are derived from explicitly stated postulates. Euclid did his work so well that the *Elements* became the model and the inspiration for other postulational systems, even outside the domain of mathematics. For example, Newton wrote his *Principia* and Spinoza tried to write his *Ethics* as a sequence of theorems derived from explicitly stated assumptions and appropriate definitions. Nevertheless, the model itself is imperfect as a postulational structure. Euclid injected circular reasoning in the form of proofs by superposition, and he left a big gap in the structure when he failed to deal with relations of order. These defects were corrected in Hilbert's axioms for Euclidean geometry. Many other ways of axiomatizing Euclidean geometry are possible. Birkhoff has prepared a set of axioms that uses *length of a line* and *angle measure* as primitive notions. Prenowitz has prepared another set of axioms built around the notion of a *convex set*. The latter two sets of axioms have been offered as having the advantage of leading to a rigorous development of Euclidean geometry that is simple enough to be within the grasp of high-school students.

I have described eight areas in which mathematics has subjected itself to searching self-criticism in order to build a rigorous foundation for its elaborate superstructure. If you reexamine what I have said about each of these eight areas you will find that I had to use the word "set" in order to describe what was done. All avenues of investigation of the foundations of mathematics converge toward set theory. In a systematic deductive development of mathematics, all constructions radiate out from set theory like the spokes of a wheel from a hub. Set-theoretic concepts are as necessary to mathematical discourse today as common nouns are to ordinary discourse. The analogy invoked by this remark, by the way, is not a superficial one, in view of the fact that every common noun defines a set.

Modern Mathematics

Modern mathematics is the direct result of the multiplicity of spaces and geometries and the multiplicity of algebraic structures developed by classical mathematics. Modern mathematics is to classical mathematics as elementary algebra is to elementary arithmetic. Elementary arithmetic deals with many numbers in the real number system. However, its statements are always assertions about relationships connecting specific numbers. Elementary algebra, on the other hand, by using variables, has a way of making assertions that are valid for many numbers or even for all numbers in the real number system. For example, whereas arithmetic may say $2 + 3 = 3 + 2$, algebra will say $x + y = y + x$. Similarly, while classical mathematics deals with many different mathematical structures, its typical approach is to study relationships in one structure at a time. Modern mathematics, on the other hand, studies at one stroke the properties of all structures of a particular type. Thus, while classical mathematics may study the real number system, which happens to be an ordered field, modern mathematics will study ordered fields in general. Naturally, whatever is discovered about ordered fields in general will apply to the real number system in particular.

The purpose of modern mathematics of dealing with many

structures at once dictates the form that it takes. Modern mathematics is necessarily axiomatic, deductive, and abstract. It defines a type of structure, such as a field, as a set of elements and relations satisfying certain axioms. As in Euclid's axiomatic treatment of geometry, it deduces theorems from the axioms. The treatment is abstract in the sense that no meanings are attached to the terms and relations used in the axioms other than those expressed by the axioms themselves. Thus, in a topological space, a point should not be understood as something that can be represented by a dot on the blackboard. It is merely an element in a set which has special subsets known as *open sets* that satisfy certain axioms. The advantage of the abstract approach is that one abstract structure may have many concrete representations. By not being tied to one interpretation of the terms, we are free to use many interpretations. Thus, there are topological spaces whose points are the points of elementary geometry. There are topological spaces whose points are the lines of elementary geometry. There are topological spaces whose points are functions. Similarly, there are many possible interpretations for the points of a Euclidean plane to which the ideal points on the "line at infinity" have been added. They may be interpreted as the lines in a bundle of lines through a point in Euclidean three-space. They may also be interpreted as certain equivalence classes of triples of real numbers.

Some of the abstract structures of modern mathematics are referred to as *algebraic structures*. Others are referred to as *geometric structures* or *spaces*. What is the distinction between them? An algebraic structure is defined by means of *operations* analogous to addition and multiplication, satisfying certain axioms. Groups, for example, are defined in terms of one operation. Rings and fields are defined in terms of two operations. A space, however, is defined by means of certain *distinguished subsets* that satisfy particular axioms. Thus, a projective space is defined in terms of the subsets called *lines,* a topological space is defined in terms of the subsets called *open sets,* and a measurable space is defined in terms of subsets called *measurable sets.*

At one time the geometry of Euclid was unique in being axiomatic and deductive. Now all mathematical structures are axiomatic and deductive. One of the arguments for teaching Euclid in the high schools used to be that it was the best vehicle for introducing young people to a deductive system. This argument is no longer valid. To introduce young people to deductive systems, we now have many deductive systems to choose from. We don't have to wait for the tenth year to do it, and we don't have to restrict deductive reasoning to the study of geometry.

A characteristic of modern mathematics is its attempt to be as general as possible. A modern mathematician is not content with proving a theorem by means of given axioms. As soon as he has proved the theorem, he tries to see how many axioms he can leave out and still prove the theorem. He tries to find out how much he can weaken his axioms and still be able to prove the theorem. In short, he is never happy with merely finding sufficient conditions for his theorem. He wants to know which conditions are also necessary. By proving a theorem with the weakest possible set of assumptions, he finds the broadest domain to which the theorem applies.

The modern mathematician is concerned with whole structures rather than individual members of the structure. His typical technique for studying a structure is to map one structure into another. Naturally a central role is played by the structure-preserving mappings known in general as *homo-*

morphisms, and as *isomorphisms* if they are one to one and onto. Thus, the algebraist uses mappings that put sums into sums and products into products. The student of projective geometry uses mappings that put lines into lines (collineations). The student of topology uses mappings that put open sets into open sets (open mappings) or, more frequently, mappings for which the inverse image of an open set is an open set (continuous mappings). The student of measure theory uses measurable functions, for which the inverse image of a measurable set is a measurable set.

The modern mathematician often uses a classical mathematical structure as the starting point of his investigations. He analyzes the structure to isolate from it certain separate qualities. He studies these qualities in abstraction in separate structures. Then he puts the structures together in various combinations. Thus he finds that the real number system may be viewed as a group, a ring, a field, an ordered set, a topological space, etc. So he studies abstractly groups, rings, fields, ordered sets, topological spaces, and so on. Then he studies such things as topological groups, topological rings, topological fields, ordered fields, etc., in which two structures are combined into one. After he has found many qualities in a given structure, he is often particularly interested in finding out how many of these qualities he must put together to obtain the original structure. For example, the real number system has these properties: (1) It is a number system in the sense that it has two operations called addition and multiplication that are associative and commutative and such that multiplication is distributive with respect to addition. (2) It is an extension of the rational number system. (3) It is ordered. (4) It has the property that any nonempty set in it which has an upper bound has a least upper bound. The interesting thing about these properties is that they characterize the real number system. Any system that has these four properties must be the real number system (that is, is isomorphic to it).

Since we have stressed the advantages of the formal deductive approach of modern mathematics, it is necessary to say something about its limitations. Not all mathematics is formal and deductive. In the first place, mathematical discovery is not deductive. The research mathematician who gropes his way toward new theorems is guided by analogy, by hunches, by trial and error, and by flashes of intuitive insight. It is only after he has made his discoveries that he uses hindsight and shows how he could have arrived at his conclusions most economically by deductive reasoning.

Secondly, a deductive system is incapable of supplying the justification for its acceptance as a legitimate mathematical system. A mathematical system is legitimate only if it is consistent, that is, free of contradiction. A proof of the consistency of a system may be developed as a theorem of metamathematics (reasoning *about* the mathematical system, but not *in* that system). But the validity of the proof depends on assuming the consistency of the system of axioms underlying the metamathematical argument. In the case of a system that is inclusive enough to contain the natural numbers of arithmetic, this assumption means taking more for granted than does the assumption that arithmetic itself is consistent. This fact follows from Gödel's theorem that such a consistency proof requires rules of inference that are even stronger than those of arithmetic. Thus, the problem of proving the consistency of arithmetic is not solved, but merely shifted to other ground. For this reason it is common practice to follow two procedures to establish the consistency of a deductive system. One procedure is to prove only *relative* consistency. For example, it is possible to prove that non-Euclidean geometry is consistent if Euclidean geometry is consistent. The second procedure is to prove the absolute consistency of a system by producing a concrete representation of it. But this, of course, involves an appeal to intuition. In constructing mathematical systems we cannot exclude intuition entirely. We can only restrict the area in which we must lean on intuition.

Even if we could do without intuition in the creation of mathematics, it would be folly to try to do without it in the teaching of mathematics. I am sure that the reader must have had the experience I have often had of following a deductive argument step by step and ending up not knowing what it was that had been proved. While a deductive argument may show us where one tree stands in relation to another, an intuitive argument is often the best way of seeing the woods that are made up of all those trees.

While we stress the limitations of deductive argument, let us not forget, meanwhile, the limitations of intuition. Intuition is a useful guide, but sometimes an unreliable one. Let us remember that intuition misled some eighteenth-century mathematicians into saying that the infinite series $1 - 1 + 1 - 1 + \ldots$ has a sum equal to $\frac{1}{2}$. What is "discovered" by intuition has to be checked by rigorous deductive argument.

Mathematics in the form of an axiomatic deductive system has sometimes been described as a game. The mathematician, it is said, makes up the rules of the game in the form of axioms. Then he proceeds to play the game according to the rules. Some people have gone beyond this assertion to say that mathematics is *only* a game, played without regard to any possible applications. This assertion is not correct. It is true that the pure mathematician should be free to explore in any direction in which his curiosity carries him. But his choice of the rules of his game is not entirely arbitrary. He tries to select rules that he and his colleagues will judge to be significant. And the measure of significance is usually the extent to which they relate to existing mathematical structures and to practical applications.

Pure mathematics has benefited greatly by growing up in intimate contact with practical applications. To see the truth of this statement we need only recall how the theory of elliptic integrals and functions grew out of the pendulum problem, how Fourier series grew out of the study of heat, how the study of Riemannian geometry was stimulated by relativity theory, and how the study of Hilbert spaces was encouraged by quantum mechanics. The greatest mathematicians have always combined dedication to pure mathematics with a strong interest in its applications. This is shown, for example, in the work of Gauss, Klein, Poincaré, Weyl and Von Neumann, to mention only a few.

The growth of modern mathematics has led to increased specialization. Specialization leads to a fragmentation by subdivision of subject matter. At the same time, however, there is a growing unification of method. Set-theoretic methods permeate all of modern mathematics. Algebraic methods reach out into topology. Topological methods are used to deal with problems in analysis, etc. For example, in algebraic topology, essentially geometric configurations are studied by the examination of associated groups. The typical technique is to set up a sequence of groups such that each group is mapped homomorphically into the next one in the sequence. Now this algebraic technique, developed originally for the study of topology, has been generalized and axiomatized in homological algebra and has become a technique of abstract algebra. Another interesting example of the trend toward unification is found in the way an existence proof in the theory of differential equations can be derived from a fixed-point theorem in topology.

There is one fact implicit in what I have said about modern mathematics that should be stated explicitly. Modern mathematics does not replace classical mathematics. It generalizes it, supplements it, unifies it, and deepens our understanding of it. But classical mathematics in the form of arithmetic, analysis, and geometry is as important as it ever was.

I would like to comment at this point on some aspects of the strategy of contemporary mathematics that are important even though they are not at all new. There are some typical methods of the mathematician that he uses in classical mathematics as well as modern mathematics. They are worth noting here because they are used in elementary mathematics as well as in advanced mathematics.

1. After defining a structure or a configuration of which there may be many examples, the mathematician frequently sets himself the task of identifying and classifying all the possible examples. For instance, algebraists are trying to identify and classify all finite groups. They have solved the classification problem for finite commutative groups. They have only scratched the surface of the problem for finite groups in general. Classification is often accomplished by picking out a set of simple cases and then expressing all other cases as combinations of the simple cases. For example, finite commutative groups are factored into products of cyclic groups. In arithmetic, integers are expressed as products of primes. In plane geometry, polygons are decomposed into triangles.

2. Often classification is accomplished by dividing the set of things being studied into equivalence classes, and then showing that each equivalence class contains one and only one ele-

ment of a special type. This is the technique of *reducing to canonical form*. In elementary algebra, for example, we reduce polynomials to the canonical form $a_0x^n + \ldots + a_n$. In arithmetic we reduce fractions to the canonical form called "lowest terms."

3. Sometimes we pick out a set of simple cases and show that although other cases cannot be reduced to these simple cases, at least they can be approximated by them. Approximation theorems occur in many branches of mathematics. In the theory of numbers, for example, there is a theorem that every real number can be approximated as closely as we please by a rational number whose denominator is not too big. Specifically, it says that if a is real and g is a positive integer, we can find integers x, y such that $|x - ay| < \dfrac{1}{g}$, with $1 \leq y \leq g$. In the theory of functions of a real variable we have the Weierstrass theorem that any continuous function on the closed segment from 0 to 1 can be approximated by polynomials. In algebraic topology, compact metric spaces are approximated by finite polyhedra. In elementary calculus and in plane geometry we often approximate a rectifiable curve by an inscribed polygon.

4. Sometimes we study a structure by seeing what happens when we map it into one of a set of simple and well-known examples of that structure. For example, a group is often studied by mapping it into a matrix group. A ring may be studied by mapping it into the ring of endomorphisms of a group (homomorphisms of the group into itself). If we map each polynomial with real coefficients into its residue class modulo $x^2 + 1$, we have a homomorphism that can be used to prove that the complex number system exists, that it is a field, that it contains the real number system as a subfield, and, of course, that it contains a square root of -1.

5. We have just described four ways in which the simplest cases of a structure or configuration are used to study the general cases. There is one technique which uses the opposite approach. It studies the general cases by paying particular attention to the exceptional, pathological case. It is analogous to the way in which psychologists learn about normal behavior by studying neuroses and psychoses. In the theory of functions of a complex variable, for example, we encounter the singular points of a function. These are the points where the function does not behave itself at all, and in fact, may not even be defined. Far from ignoring the singular points, we pay particular attention to them, because they have a great influence on the behavior of the function at the points near the singularity. The function behaves in one way near a pole, and in a different way near an essential singularity. Similarly, in the theory of systems of ordinary linear differential equations, we find it to our advantage to examine the critical point of the system (the place where all components of the derivative vanish), because the nature of the solutions to the system of equations depends on what happens in the neighborhood of the critical point. In elementary calculus we use a similar approach to help us do curve tracing by first identifying the pathological cases: the discontinuities, the maxima and minima, and the points of inflection.

6. An interesting feature of many branches of mathematics is the existence of *duality*. Wherever duality occurs, a theorem can immediately be translated into a dual theorem without any further proof. In projective plane geometry, point and line are dual to each other. In projective three-space, point and plane are dual to each other. In linear algebra, a vector space over a scalar field and the set of linear mappings of the space into the scalar field are dual to each other. In elementary plane geom-

etry, there is an imperfect duality of point and line, and a related duality of side and angle in a polygon. In spherical geometry, there is the duality of great circle and pole. Conscious use of duality, where it exists, makes possible the discovery of new relationships and affords a deeper insight into the relationships that hold a structure together.

Mathematics More and More Intimately Related to Man's Activities

While mathematics, in the form of pure mathematics, has reached dizzying heights of abstraction, it has kept its feet on the ground by multiplying and extending its applications.

Now more than ever, it is true that mathematics is the handmaiden of the sciences. Before this century the science of physics had already made abundant use of mathematics in mechanics, optics, the theory of heat, and electromagnetic theory. Analysis used to be the chief mathematical tool of the physicist. Now, with the development of relativity theory and quantum mechanics, he has had to learn Riemannian geometry and modern algebra. The increasing role that chance processes play in physical theory compels him to learn probability theory as well.

Mathematics has spilled over from physics into the other physical sciences, chemistry and geology. It has invaded the life sciences, biology and psychology, and has expanded into the social sciences too. There is no area of science today that can avoid using mathematical methods.

With the growing complexity of industrial and business life, industry and commerce have raised more and more questions that can be answered adequately only by the use of mathematical methods. Insurance and pension systems use actuarial mathematics. Industries undertaking quality control use statistical methods. Commercial establishments choose from among alternative courses of action with the help of linear programming. Military strategists plan their moves with the help of the theory of games. Communications engineers use information theory and Boolean algebra.

To deal with complicated problems at high speed, automatic electronic computers have been constructed. Mathematicians share in the designing of the computers and in setting up their programs. Because of the widespread use of computers, logarithms have lost their importance as a computational tool.

To meet the new demands made by science, industry and government, mathematics has had to grow in new directions. There is a vigorous development of the theory of differential equations and methods of solving them by means of computers. There has been a tremendous growth in the theories of probability and statistics. New areas of study, such as linear programming, the theory of games, and information theory, have sprung up overnight.

The spread of automation in industry is changing the character of the labor force. The tendency is to reduce the amount of unskilled and semiskilled labor that is used, and to increase the need for technically trained personnel with a knowledge of mathematics. The importance of mathematics in vocational training will continue to grow in the future.

The production of food, clothing and shelter has never been man's sole concern. He has always found it necessary to ponder over deep questions about man's relation to man and about his place in the universe. Even these questions have now taken on a mathematical character. I shall refer to only two obvious examples. For thousands of years philosophers have had endless debates about the meaning of infinity. Now it is impossible to talk sense on this subject without taking into account what mathematics has contributed through the theory of the continuum and of transfinite numbers. In the past, philosophers have speculated about the nature of space. Is it finite or infinite? Is it bounded or unbounded? Now it is impossible to talk sense about these questions without taking into account what Riemannian geometry has contributed through the theory of relativity. Mathematics is increasingly important as an essential ingredient of a liberal education.

Suggested Readings for Chapter 3

Adler, Irving, *A New Look at Geometry*. New York, The John Day Company.

——, *Probability and Statistics for Everyman*. New York, The John Day Company.

——, *The New Mathematics*. New York, The John Day Company.

——, *Thinking Machines*. New York, The John Day Company.

Aleksandrov, A. D., Kolmogorov, A. N., and Lavrent'ev, M.A., editors, *Mathematics, Its Content, Methods and Meaning*. Cambridge, The M. I. T. Press.

Newman, James R., *The World of Mathematics*. New York, Simon & Schuster.

4.] Curriculum Change: For Whom, and for What Purpose?

■ SHALL begin by stating the premises on which this chapter is based. I assume that continuing revision of the mathematics curriculum is necessary and desirable. I assume that the changes sponsored by the Commission on Mathematics of the College Entrance Examination Board, the Secondary School Curriculum Committee of the National Council of Teachers of Mathematics, the University of Illinois Committee on School Mathematics, and the School Mathematics Study Group are basically sound. I shall not present the arguments in favor of these changes because they are well known and, by this time, widely accepted. I assume therefore that the movement for curriculum change initiated by these groups should be strengthened in every way by the retraining of teachers, the preparation of suitable teaching materials, and the elaboration of appropriate methods of teaching, so that teachers will be fully equipped to use the modified courses of study in the schools.

I shall confine my remarks to two questions about the movement for curriculum revision: What are the goals toward which the changes in the curriculum are directed? For which pupils is the revised curriculum appropriate?

Let us consider first the goals of curriculum revision. In the discussion about curriculum change it is said that we must bring our courses of study up to date so that we may better accomplish certain desirable aims. I find that considerable stress is given to three aims in particular:

1. The training of mathematicians. Mathematics is a living, growing science. By giving our best students an early introduction to the concepts and style of thinking of modern mathematics, we hasten the day when, as research mathematicians, they will help to push forward the frontier of mathematical knowledge.

2. The training of members of the professions that use mathematics in their daily work. Mathematics has always been an indispensable tool for the physicist, the statistician, and the engineer. It is rapidly becoming one for the biologist, the psychologist, and the economist.

3. The training of mathematics teachers. With science and industry using more and more mathematics, both classical and modern, and with school enrolments growing at a rapid pace, we need more and more mathematics teachers whose training is thorough and modern in spirit.

These three aims have one feature in common: They relate to the vocational goals of the schools. But there are also non-vocational aims of mathematics instruction that are of equal importance. I shall discuss two of these: (*a*) the development of the kind of literacy that is needed by a citizen in a complex, industrial society in the era of automation and nuclear energy;

and (*b*) cultivation of the intellect and liberation of the mind.

Mathematics teachers have always felt that the concept of literacy in our society should have a broader meaning than that usually attributed to it. In a society based on advanced technology and revolving around the market, it is not enough that the citizen be able to read and write. He has to know how to count, measure and compute. In a society in which rapid change is the rule, he can hope to understand how changes are related to each other only if he knows what a variable is, knows the meaning of a function in the mathematical sense, and knows how to derive and interpret rates of change. In a society made up of aggregates of people producing aggregates of commodities composed of aggregates of physical particles, he has to understand the concepts that have evolved out of the study of aggregates. He has to know how to interpret the words *and* and *or,* and he should understand the meaning of such terms as "average," "probable," and "correlated." In a society that has cultivated to a high degree the art of travel in a Riemannian plane—namely, the surface of the earth—and is now beginning to leave that plane in order to explore three-dimensional space without knowing whether it is Euclidean, Riemannian or Lobatschewskian, he should have some understanding of spatial relationships. In short, in order to understand what his neighbor, his co-worker, his newspaper, or his government is saying, the modern citizen must know some mathematics as well as English.

Many branches of mathematics contribute to the development of this broader and deeper kind of literacy. Arithmetic, algebra, geometry, probability theory, and the calculus all play their parts. With the bias that is typical of algebraists, I hasten to add that all of these are elaborations of various aspects of the number systems of everyday use. So the core of teaching for mathematical literacy is the development of an understanding of numbers and their uses. It is not without reason, then, that reading, writing and arithmetic have always been considered the backbone of education. One of the virtues of the new curriculum that is emerging now is that, far from displacing the traditional study of arithmetic, it deepens it and strengthens it with new insights. It changes arithmetic from a loose jumble of disconnected rules to be memorized into a beautiful structure whose internal relationships can be understood. It is a thrilling experience to hear eighth- or ninth-grade pupils who have been taught from the new course of study. They talk with ease about such things as the distributive law, the zero principle, the unity principle, and additive and multiplicative inverses. And, what is more, they know what they are talking about. They see these concepts and principles used when they add or multiply fractions, factor a polynomial, or solve an equation, and as a result they understand what they are doing. Experience with the new courses of study in arithmetic and algebra shows that they are more effective than the old ones in developing the skills and insights that constitute mathematical literacy.

Mathematics teachers have always been convinced that the teaching of mathematics has a unique contribution to make to the cultivation of a student's intellect, to the development of his ability to think. It is true that for a while the psychologists turned against us and said that our conviction was unfounded because there is no transfer of training. But we stood our ground and waited patiently for them to change their minds, and they did. Meanwhile we went about our business, teaching young people the nature of deductive reasoning, guiding them in the detection of hidden assumptions and fallacious arguments, training them to be precise in their thinking and speech, and encouraging them to be critical of sweeping generalizations. We did this with our old curricular materials. We do it even better with the revised curriculum.

There are some people who are afraid that the stress on mathematics and science today represents a weakening of liberal education. We mathematics teachers do not share this fear. If a liberal education is one that liberates the mind, mathematics can play an important part in a liberal education. To demonstrate this fact, let me give some examples of mathematics that frees the mind. These examples are drawn from the new content that is being introduced into our courses of study and they reflect the new outlook in the teaching of mathematics.

One example is noncommutative multiplication. Multiplication of real numbers is a commutative operation. That is, if x and y are real numbers, then the product xy is equal to the product yx. This fact is implicit in some of the algorithms we teach the children, but in the past we rarely if ever stated the fact explicitly. Now we do state it explicitly so that the children may use this property of real numbers consciously and deliberately. In order to sharpen their appreciation of this property, we introduce them to some structures in which a multiplication operation is defined that is not commutative. We may use for this purpose a one-operation structure like a group of permutations, or a two-operation structure like the ring of 2 by 2 matrices whose elements are integers. For example, if x and y are members of a group of permutations, then the product xy need not be equal to the product yx. Children who have had experience with both commutative and noncommutative multiplications learn that familiar structures are not the only possible or the only legitimate structures. This is an important lesson in open-mindedness.

A second example is given by finite fields. Among the most useful properties of the real number system are those that it has by virtue of being a field. But the real number system is not the only field that exists. Fields that are suitable for study on the elementary-school level are the finite fields with a prime number of elements. They are easily defined by means of clockface diagrams. For example, a clockface whose circumference is divided into five equal parts by points labeled 0, 1, 2, 3 and 4 respectively can be used to define a field with five elements. Addition may be denied by successive motions around the clockface, and multiplication may be defined by means of repeated addition. Then the addition and multiplication tables are easily derived. The multiplication table helps to clarify the meaning of the fact that in a field every non-zero element has a unique multiplicative inverse, and the related fact that in a field an equation of the form $ax = b$, where a is not zero, is always solvable and has a unique root. The axioms of a field are fairly strong axioms. Experience with finite fields helps to show that they leave room nevertheless for considerable variety of structure. Recognition of the existence of diversity in unity is an important lesson for young minds. Besides, children are fascinated and excited by finite fields. They are drawn to these miniature number systems by the same esthetic impulse that makes them love scale models, kittens, and toy trains.

A third example consists of rings with a zero divisor. If, in a ring, there are elements a and b which are not equal to zero, but whose product is equal to zero, then each of the elements a and b is called a *zero divisor*. It is easy to introduce children to a ring with zero divisors by using a clockface diagram in which the number of equal parts into which the circumference is divided is not a prime. Addition and multiplication in the ring can be defined in the same way as they were for the field of five elements described above. The result is a miniature number system that is like a field in some respects but unlike it in others. For example, in the miniature number system derived from a clockface diagram divided into six equal parts, the elements of the system are the numbers 0, 1, 2, 3, 4 and 5. In this system, the numbers 3 and 2 are zero divisors, because although neither 3 nor 2 is zero, the product 3×2 is equal to zero. Because of this fact, the equation $3x = 0$ in this miniature number system has a non-zero root, $x = 2$, as well as the root $x = 0$. So the rule that if $ab = 0$, and a is not 0, then $b = 0$, which is valid in a field, is not valid in this ring. Experience with this fact helps children to appreciate that all rules have limitations. There is a domain in which a rule is valid. Once you step out of that domain the rule may break down.

We have a fourth example in transfinite numbers. Children working with numbers will naturally ask, "How many are there?" By comparing the cardinal numbers of the natural number system, the rational number system, and the real number system, we can give them meaningful answers to this question. At the same time we admit them to a fascinating world of paradox, where the whole may be equal to one of its proper parts, where the infinite may be contained within the finite, and where the continuous is made up of the discrete. The expanded concept of cardinal number, embracing transfinite as well as finite numbers, is a mind-stretching idea that relates everyday activities like counting and measuring to some deep philosophical questions.

A fifth example is non-Euclidean geometry. This subject arises naturally in the study of spherical geometry, since a hemisphere in which diametrically opposite points of the bounding circle are identified is a Riemannian plane. Through contact with non-Euclidean geometry, young people learn that a question like "What is the sum of the angles of a triangle?" must be given a qualified answer. *If* the space is Euclidean, the sum is 180°. *If* the space is Riemannian, the sum is more than 180°, and so on. They learn in this way that all conclusions obtained by deduction have a relative character. They learn to look for the assumptions on which an argument is based. This is an experience in critical thinking that is invaluable for people who will live in a world of competing propagandas. Through non-Euclidean geometry they also make contact with one of the great unsolved problems of cosmology: is the physical universe Euclidean, Riemannian or Lobatschewskian?

As a final example, I cite the geometry of *n* dimensions, with *n* greater than 3. Once young people have learned, through the use of Cartesian coordinates, that plane geometry is a geometry of *ordered pairs* of real numbers, and that solid geometry is a geometry of *ordered triples,* there is no difficulty about introducing the idea of a geometry of *ordered n-tuples.* This idea breaks the shackles of three-dimensional intuition and frees the mind to explore worlds that are unseen.

The six examples I have given suffice to prove my point. The new courses of study that we are developing enhance the contribution that the study of mathematics makes to a liberal education. They stimulate the imagination and cultivate thinking that is rigorous but not rigid. They encourage open-mindedness, a critical outlook, and flexibility of thought.

We turn now to the second question I have raised. For which pupils is the revised curriculum appropriate? Our answer to this question will depend on our understanding of the goals toward which the revised curriculum is directed. If we consider only the vocational goals of training mathematicians or scientists or teachers, we are led naturally to one conclusion: that this is a curriculum for the gifted student, or at best for the somewhat larger group of college-bound students. If the purpose of the new curriculum is exclusively the development of professional competence, it is suitable only for those young people who are preparing to enter the professions. However, we have seen that there are *other* purposes, not of a vocational character, that the new curriculum serves as well. These are the purposes of developing mathematical literacy, and cultivating and liberating the mind. These purposes are relevant for *all* pupils, not merely the gifted or the college-bound. Consequently the new courses of study should not be restricted to the college-bound, but should be extended to all pupils.

Some teachers will react to this suggestion by saying, "You are asking for the impossible. The new course of study introduces abstractions and generalizations and a level of rigorous thinking that is beyond the ability of the average student. It may be all right for the high-I.Q. child, but it is too difficult for anyone else." To see if there is any merit to this argument, let's analyze the concept of the "impossible," and then give a little thought to the meaning of the I.Q.

During World War II, among the first to land on a newly captured island in the Pacific were the Seabees (the Construction Battalions). A magazine article describing their work said they were guided by the slogan: "The difficult we do immediately. The impossible takes a little longer." This slogan epitomizes a common attitude toward the concept of the impossible. In this age of orbital flights around the earth and rockets that land on the moon, we tend to think that nothing is really impossible. We incline to the belief that with hard work and ingenuity almost any goal can be attained. This outlook shows commendable enthusiasm, but is it always realistic? As mathematicians we know that there are times when it is not. Some things are really impossible. We know, for example, that it is impossible to trisect an arbitrary angle with a straight edge and compasses alone. To use an example that is more familiar to young people and more easily understood, it is impossible for a baseball game to end with a score of 4½ to 3.

It is instructive for us to examine these two impossibilities and see what it is that makes them impossible. A baseball game is played according to definite rules. Under these rules the number of runs attained by a team is necessarily a non-negative integer. Under these rules, the set of all theoretically possible final scores is the set of all ordered pairs of unequal non-negative integers. A score of 4½ to 3 is impossible because it is not compatible with the rules of the game. In the classical geometric construction problems, we are also engaged in a game that is played according to definite rules. The rules specify that a circle may be drawn when you know its radius and center, and a line may be drawn when you know two of its points. Under these rules, the degree of the defining equation of a constructible quantity must be a power of two. Unfortunately the defining equation for the trisection problem has degree 3. So trisection of an angle is impossible because it is not compatible with the prescribed rule that a straightedge and compasses be used.

These two examples illustrate a general rule. In any game, a goal is impossible to attain if it is incompatible with the rules of the game. But this rule does more than tell us why some things are impossible. It also indicates how, in dealing with practical problems, we can change the *impossible* into the *possible. If a desirable goal is impossible under one set of rules, don't throw up your hands in despair. Just change the rules.* For example, trisection of an angle is *possible* if you permit instruments other than a straightedge and compasses to be used.

Now let us see what bearing this has on the claim that it is impossible to teach the new courses of study in mathematics to classes of average children. The basis of this claim is the widely accepted view that the new content can be mastered only by the superior child, usually defined as having an I.Q. of 120 or more. This view in turn is based on the most common conception of what the I.Q. means.

The prevalent theory of the I.Q. asserts that it measures innate intelligence and indicates an upper limit to the intellectual performance that may be expected of a child. Many people accept this assertion as an established fact. On the contrary, it is only an unproved hypothesis. Moreover, it is a hypothesis that is intrinsically unprovable. It is as valid to attribute a child's performance on an intelligence test to his heredity rather than his environment as it is to attribute the area of a rectangle to its base rather than its altitude.

The main question for us to consider now is what happens when teachers accept this unproved hypothesis and act as if it were established fact. The practice of teaching may be thought of as a game. Our beliefs about the nature of children become part of the rules of the game. Our beliefs determine our actions, and then influence the outcomes of these actions. What are the outcomes that are more or less predetermined by acceptance of the I.Q. theory? Those who rely on the I.Q. theory assume that most children are not capable of learning much. A natural consequence is that they do not try to teach them much. They offer these children watered-down courses devoid of significant mathematical content. They take pupil failure for granted, and so neither teacher nor child is required to exert the effort that might prevent failure. The major result is cumulative retardation from year to year. The child becomes less and less prepared to cope with the work of the higher grades. This process of educational decay is self-reinforcing, because it is controlled by a typical feedback loop: We think the children are not capable of learning, so we teach them less. Then they learn less, and become less capable of learning. So again we teach them less, and so an ad infinitum. Teachers and pupils become trapped in a vicious circle.

Under these circumstances it is quite true that it is impossible to teach the new courses, with their richer mathematical content, to the children whose school performance is weak. However, it is impossible only within the framework of the rules by which we operate. It is impossible largely because of the deleterious effects of the I.Q. theory and the school practices based on it. But we can break out of the vicious circle in which we are trapped. We can convert the impossible into the possible by changing the rules of our game. Let us cut the feedback loop by throwing overboard the I.Q. theory and the defeatist attitude that it engenders. Replace the I.Q. theory with a new, yet really old, hypothesis: that all children except those with serious brain damage are capable of learning and thinking; they are able to master abstractions and generalizations if they are properly taught. So let us not hold back from any children the benefits of the new courses of study. Extend the new program to all classes on all levels.

What I am recommending will not be easy to accomplish. We cannot blow away overnight the accumulated effects of decades of retardation. We cannot substitute mere wishes for accomplishment. Success will not be automatic. It will be attained only through great effort. If we undertake to teach genuine mathematics to all children, there are many difficult problems that we shall have to face and solve. We shall have to think through very carefully the problem of grade placement of the various concepts and skills we want to develop. We shall have to select appropriate teaching methods suited to the age and maturity of the child. We shall have to pace our lessons differently for children with different levels of preparation. But we shall have to do so without robbing them of content. We shall have to keep in mind at all times the old familiar rules of good teaching: from the specific to the general; from the concrete to the abstract. But above all, we shall have to find more effective ways of motivating our pupils, so that they willingly exert themselves in order to gain the rich rewards of learning.

Let us reassert our confidence in the children of the United States, and we shall be able to do the impossible, even if it does take a little longer.

Suggested Readings for Chapter 4

Adler, Irving, *A New Look at Geometry*. New York, The John Day Company.

———, *The New Mathematics*. New York, The John Day Company.

———, *What We Want of Our Schools* (Chapter IV). New York, The John Day Company.

5.] Mathematics for the Low Achiever

A NEW approach to the low achiever in mathematics is beginning to take hold in the secondary schools of the United States.

The old approach, dominant in the 1930s and 1940s, was based on the unproved assumption that the low achiever is primarily a person with low innate ability. Because of his supposed low capacity for learning, we put a ceiling on our expectations for him. If a ninth-grade student with an I.Q. of 80 performed on the level of the average sixth-grade student, we called his work "satisfactory" because he was "working up to the level of his ability." We classified him as "nonacademically minded," implying by this label that he was incapable of dealing with abstractions, and was best kept busy "doing" things with his hands rather than grappling with mathematical ideas. We assigned him to a general mathematics class where he repeated the same dull routines in "social arithmetic" that had frustrated and repelled him in earlier grades. The net effect of this approach was that the pupil's retardation in mathematics was perpetuated. The "second track" led to a dead end.

The new approach is based on the recognition that low

achievement in mathematics may be the result of many causes: low innate ability, inadequate motivation, emotional disturbances, cultural deprivation in homes of low socio-economic status, and even poor teaching in the lower grades. Inherent in this new approach is the assumption that the low achiever is probably capable of doing better if only we can identify and counteract the causes of his poor performance. On the basis of this new approach, the school tries to *overcome* the pupil's handicaps instead of perpetuating them. It tries to prepare him and encourage him to enter the regular sequence of mathematics courses at a later time.

The new-style general mathematics curriculum is not dominated by a self-defeating narrowly utilitarian point of view. It has the same general education goals as the regular curriculum designed for the average and above-average student: the development of the kind of mathematical literacy that is needed by a citizen in a complex industrial society in the era of automation and nuclear energy; and the cultivation of the intellect and liberation of the mind. To achieve these goals, the new type of program introduces the low achiever to *significant new mathematical ideas;* helps him to *relearn arithmetic* from a new, more meaningful and more mature point of view; seeks to *arouse* and *maintain his interest* in mathematics; provides him with opportunities to make genuine *mathematical discoveries* at his level of knowledge and performance; and *crystallizes his learning experience* in ideas that he understands, generalizations that he perceives and verbalizes, and skills that he masters.

Introducing Significant New Mathematical Ideas

A ninth-grade course for low achievers can include such significant new mathematical ideas as negative numbers, permutations, combinations, probability, and indirect measurement via the tangent ratio and the Pythagorean theorem. The treatment of these topics differs from that in the ordinary algebra class in at least three ways: there is more reliance on specific and concrete examples, visual aids, and manual activity in developing the underlying concepts; the lessons are paced more slowly; the concepts are applied only to simple situations where the underlying principle stands out in sharp relief. For example, to teach the addition of algebraic numbers, positive and negative numbers are represented first as points on the number line, then as motions on the number line. Positive numbers are represented by motions to the right. Negative numbers are represented by motions to the left. Addition of numbers is carried out by performing two motions in succession. For example, to add 2 and -5, the student starts with his pencil point at 0 and moves it two units to the right. Then he moves the pencil point five units to the left. The sum is represented by the final position of the pencil point.

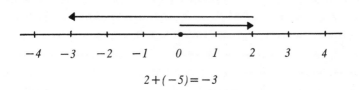

$$2+(-5)=-3$$

Addition on the Number Line

The student can also make a slide rule that performs the addition automatically. The slide rule consists of two strips of cardboard, each bearing the scale shown above. To add 2 and -5, the zero of the upper scale is placed over the 2 on the lower scale. The student then locates -5 on the upper scale. Directly under it on the lower scale is the sum of 2 and -5.

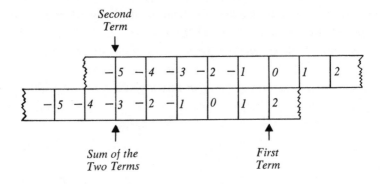

A Slide Rule for Addition

The student does all additions on the number line or on the slide rule until he discovers by himself a way of doing the addition mentally.

Relearning Arithmetic

The low achiever has not mastered the four fundamental operations of arithmetic. We can revive his flagging interest in arithmetic by teaching these old concepts in a new setting as applications of the basic structure properties of the number system: the commutative laws, the associative laws, the distributive law, the law of zero, and the law of 1. For example, the student develops a better understanding of the usual way of multiplying 3×15 if he first does it in two other ways, as follows:

Applying the distributive law:

$3 \times 15 = 3 \times (10 + 5)$

$\quad\quad\quad = (3 \times 10) + (3 \times 5)$

$\quad\quad\quad = 30 + 15$

$\quad\quad\quad = 45$

$$\begin{array}{r} 15 \\ \times 3 \\ \hline 3 \times 5 = 15 \\ 3 \times 10 = 30 \\ \hline 45 \end{array}$$

He acquires a deeper insight into the meaning of the reduction of fractions if he is taught to do it by using the law of 1:

$$\frac{6}{8} = \frac{3 \times 2}{4 \times 2} = \frac{3}{4} \times \frac{2}{2} = \frac{3}{4} \times 1 = \frac{3}{4}.$$

In addition to relearning the meaning of the operations in arithmetic, the low achiever must practice using them until he masters them. However, practice exercises need not be given in the form of arbitrary and dull drill routines. The practice can be provided in a meaningful setting that arouses interest and encourages sustained effort. For example, the pupil gets a good deal of practice in addition and multiplication when he performs the following task, which all children find intrinsically interesting: Write the base-ten numerals 27 and 13 as base-five numerals. Multiply the base-five numerals. Check your answer by multiplying the base-ten numerals and comparing the answers.

$27_{\text{ten}} = 1$ twenty-five $+ 0$ fives $+ 2$ ones $= 102_{\text{five}}.$
$13_{\text{ten}} = 0$ twenty-fives $+ 2$ fives $+ 3$ ones $= 23_{\text{five}}.$

Base five *multiplication:*	*Base ten* *multiplication:*
102	27
$\times 23$	$\times 13$
311	81
204	27
2401	351

Note: $3 \times (2 \text{ ones}) = 6 \text{ ones} = 1 \text{ five} + 1 \text{ one} = 11_{\text{five}}.$
   $1 \text{ five} + 4 \text{ fives} = 5 \text{ fives} = 1 \text{ twenty-five} = 100_{\text{five}}.$
Check: $2401_{\text{five}} = [(2 \times 125) + (4 \times 25) + (0 \times 5) + (1 \times 1)]_{\text{ten}} = (250 + 100 + 0 + 1)_{\text{ten}} = 351_{\text{ten}}.$

Arousing and Maintaining Interest

There are many devices that may be used to keep the student's interest at a high level. First, give the student the feeling that he is always learning something new, even when he is reviewing an old topic. The examples cited above show how this can be done with the four fundamental operations of arithmetic. Secondly, as far as possible, use problems that are intrinsically interesting. For example, in studying the representation of data by a formula, table, or graph, use such data as the variation of the frequency of a cricket's chirping with the temperature, the distance a body falls from rest in a given number of seconds, and the stopping distance of a car traveling at a given speed. Thirdly, wherever you can, present problems in the form of a challenging game. For example, the problem of writing a number as a base-five numeral can be presented as the *game of five:* A sequence of trays has values 1, 5, and 25 as shown in the drawing. A counter placed in a tray takes on the value of the tray. The aim of the game is to represent any given number by placing the fewest possible counters into the trays. The drawing gives the solution for 63. The solution shows that $63_{ten} = 223_{five}$.

| 25 | 5 | 1 |

Providing Opportunities for Discovery

A pupil who has done many additions of algebraic numbers on the number line will be able to discover for himself the usual rules for addition. A pupil who has used many tree diagrams to find all possible permutations of two out of three objects (see the diagram below) or three out of four objects, etc., will soon discover the rule for computing the number of permutations of n things taken r at a time. By allowing the pupil to make these discoveries himself, we give him the opportunity to experience the thrill of real discovery and pride in real accomplishment.

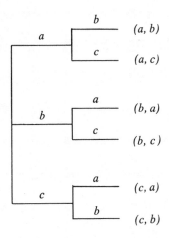

All Possible Arrangements of Two
of the Three Letters a, b and c

Crystallizing the Learning Experience

While using an abundance of concrete illustrative material and providing many opportunities for the pupil to make his own discoveries, we must be careful not to take for granted the student's ability to use what he has learned. It is not enough for the student to understand why we proceed as we do in multiplication; he must do enough multiplication to acquire facility with it. It is not enough for the student to grasp the meaning of addition on the number line; he should be led to discover the usual rule for addition, to formulate this rule accurately in his own words, and then to apply the rule so that he is no longer dependent on the graphic method based on the number line. It is not enough for the student to solve permutation problems with a tree diagram; he should develop the general formula for linear permutations and learn how to use it.

The new approach to teaching the low achiever combines rediscovery of the old with advance into the new, discovery with application, understanding with mastery, and interest with effort. In this way it raises him to ever higher levels of achievement.

Suggested Readings for Chapter 5

Adler, Irving, *A New Look at Arithmetic*. New York, The John Day Company.

————, *Magic House of Numbers*. New York, The John Day Company.

————, *What We Want of Our Schools* (Chapter IV). New York, The John Day Company.

Adler, Irving and Ruth, *Numbers Old and New*. New York, The John Day Company.

————, *Numerals: New Dresses for Old Numbers*. New York, The John Day Company.

————, *Sets*. New York, The John Day Company.

National Council of Teachers of Mathematics, *Experiences in Mathematical Discovery*.

United States Office of Education, *The Low Achiever in Mathematics*. Bulletin OE-29061, U.S. Department of Health, Education and Welfare.

6.] The Cambridge Conference Report: Blueprint or Fantasy?

■N the title of this chapter I ask two questions: Is the Cambridge Conference Report a blueprint giving detailed directions for the construction of the mathematics curriculum of the future? Or is it a fantasy that substitutes wishful thinking for an attempt to outline realistic goals that can be attained with flesh-and-blood pupils and teachers? I shall answer both questions immediately: It is neither. The rest of the chapter consists of elaboration and documentation of this answer.

The Cambridge Conference of 1963 was organized on the initiative of Professors Jerrold R. Zacharias and William Ted Martin of the Massachusetts Institute of Technology. Under the direction of Professor Martin and Professor Andrew M. Gleason of Harvard, it brought together twenty-five mathematicians and scientists to consider what changes ought to be and might be made in the precollege mathematics curriculum during the next few decades. The goal of the conference may be described as an attempt to forecast the shape and content of the mathematics curriculum of the year 1990. Among those who participated in the conference were Professors Begle,

Davis, Moise and Suppes, who have played a leading part in shaping the curriculum of today by their activities during the last two decades.

The findings of the conference were published in a report called *Goals for School Mathematics,* now usually referred to merely as the Cambridge Report. The report was drafted by Professors Davis, Gleason, Lomon, Moise and Springer, and then revised after a critical reading by a special committee that included Frank Allen, Max Beberman, and Walter Prenowitz, who had not been present at the conference.

There are three parts to the report. The first part consists of several chapters dealing with goals, pedagogical principles, and techniques. The second part contains outlines for a proposed curriculum for grades K to twelve. There is one outline for grades K to six, reflecting the common thinking of all the participants in the conference. There are two different outlines for grades seven to twelve, reflecting a major difference of opinion that developed during the discussion of what should be taught in these grades. The third part of the report consists of some of the working papers that had been presented at the conference.

The main conclusion of the report is stated in these words: ". . . A student who has worked through the full thirteen years of mathematics in grades K to twelve should have a level of training comparable to three years of top-level college training today; that is, we shall expect him to have the equivalent of two years of calculus, and one semester each of modern algebra and probability theory."

This immediately raises the question: How will it be possible to compress into thirteen years what is now spread out in sixteen years of work? The report answers this question by saying, "We propose to gain three years through a new organization of the subject matter and the virtually total abandonment of drill for drill's sake, replacing the unmotivated drill of classical arithmetic by problems which illustrate new mathematical concepts."

The report divides the precollege curriculum into three parts: grades K to two, grades three to six, and grades seven to twelve. To convey to you the spirit in which the report was written, I shall describe briefly some features of the recommendations made for each of these three parts of the curriculum.

The report proposes that the objective for mathematics instruction in the elementary grades, K to six, should be the development of familiarity with the real number system and the main ideas of geometry. To implement this proposal in grades K to two, it suggests that the number line, including negatives, be used from the very beginning. It suggests an early introduction to the idea of inequalities and to the idea of "the neighborhood of a point" on the number line. It emphasizes the use of physical interpretations of addition and multiplication, and the discovery by the children of the commutative nature of addition and multiplication. It proposes that the children deal with problems such as multiplication of a number "a little bit more than three" by a number "a little bit less than five." It also proposes the use of a box as a placeholder in simple algebraic problems. It recommends an introduction to Cartesian coordinates through appropriate games; experience with the additive property of area, closely integrated with the operation of multiplication; and experience with the symmetries of certain plane and solid figures. It also suggests the early use of sets and the concept of a function. This, of course, is only a partial list of topics proposed for grades K to two. For these early grades the report emphasizes strongly that children can study mathematics more satisfactorily when each child has abundant opportunity to manipulate suitable physical objects.

In grades three to six, the main objective is still to develop familiarity with the real number system and geometry. During these grades the pupils will learn about the commutative, associative and distributive laws, and the properties of the numbers 0 and 1. They will be introduced to the arithmetic of signed numbers. To get a better appreciation of the significance of the properties of the real number system, they will compare them with the properties of clockface number systems, finite fields, and the system of 2×2 matrices. They will learn the distinction between rational and irrational numbers, and will be introduced to the completeness property of the real number system via nested intervals. Other topics that are proposed for these grades include Cartesian coordinates and polar coordinates; vectors; truth tables for the simplest connectives; the concept of indirect proof; explicit study of the relation of open sentences and their truth sets; the concepts of isomorphism and transformation; intuitive consideration of infinite sequences of real numbers; the solution of simple algebraic equations; and many more topics, both old and new for these grades.

In the elementary grades the work is described as "premathematical." The study of formal mathematical structures is scheduled to begin in grade seven.

The two outlines proposed for grades seven to twelve have many common features. In both outlines, algebra and probability theory are assigned to grades seven and eight; linear algebra is assigned to grade ten; analysis, including infinite sequences and series, calculus, and differential equations, is assigned to grades eleven and twelve. Both outlines suggest that the study of geometry should include the study of geometric transformations.

The two outlines differ from each other in two major respects: One outline starts the study of axiomatic geometry in grades seven and eight; the other one starts it in grade nine. One outline has an introduction to calculus in grade nine and to infinite sequences and series in grade ten; the other outline delays all work in analysis until grades eleven and twelve.

I have not attempted to list all the topics proposed for each part of the curriculum. I have selected for mention chiefly those that represent a radical departure from the traditional curriculum. This does not mean that the proposed course of study neglects the traditional content of elementary-school and high-school mathematics. On the contrary, all the traditional content is there, reorganized and integrated with the equivalent of three additional years of work.

Throughout the report its authors emphasize that the findings of the conference are only tentative, and that they are submitted as the basis of a nationwide discussion by all mathematics teachers. At this stage of their development, the authors say, the views expressed in the report cannot pretend to be guidelines for school administrators or teachers. They hope that the report will be subjected to widespread discussion and that many of the proposals in it will be tested in use. The authors emphasize that nothing in the report is intended to exclude any better ideas that may arise elsewhere. Here, then, is the answer to the first question that I raise in the title of this chapter. The report is not and is not intended to be a blueprint for the curriculum of the future. It is a general statement of a goal to be reached, with a description of two different paths that may be followed to reach that goal, and an invitation to the teaching community to propose other possible paths.

I turn now to a detailed consideration of the second question: Is the goal proposed by the Cambridge Report an unrealizable fantasy, or is it a realistic goal that we should take very seriously?

Before we try to form a judgment on this question, we have to take into account a significant way in which the changes proposed in the report differ from the changes in the curriculum during the last ten years. The recent curriculum movement, as typified, let us say, by the work of the School Mathematics Study Group (SMSG), introduced changes in the middle of the curriculum first, namely in the junior-high-school curriculum, and then moved outward from there to higher and lower grades. It will not be possible to follow the same procedure with the changes proposed by the Cambridge Conference. The junior-high-school curriculum proposed by the Cambridge Report will be within the reach of pupils in grades seven, eight and nine only if they are prepared for it by the kind of curriculum that the report proposes for grades K to six. Therefore, if the kind of curriculum that the report proposes is to be introduced at all, it must be introduced systematically grade by grade, starting with the kindergarten. For this reason, when we try to judge the practicality of any part of the program for pupils of a particular grade, we must base our judgment not on the present level of preparation of the pupils of that grade, but on the level of preparation that they would have if the program were already in effect in the earlier grades.

The chief question that we must answer is this: Can children really learn in thirteen years what we now teach in sixteen years? There are two parts to this question: Can the children really learn so much? Can they learn at an early age the sophisticated mathematics that has traditionally been taught at a later age?

We will all agree at once that the answer is yes for the bright student. But can we also give an affirmative answer for the average student and for the student who is retarded even by the standards of today? It would be a grave error to assume that what students learn today is all that they are capable of learning. What they learn today depends to a great extent on what we try to teach them and the methods we use for teaching them. If the contents of our courses are attractive and meaningful and the methods used are psychologically sound, I am confident that we will be able to raise the general level of mathematical achievement in the country at approximately the pace proposed in the report. This confidence is based on twenty years of experience as a high-school teacher, often teaching classes of so-called slow learners. My experience taught me that children can learn much more than we think they can, and deeper ideas than we think they can. I find ample confirmation of my experience in the experience of others. For example, the Madison Project has recently been working at the elementary and junior-high-school level with culturally deprived children in St. Louis and Chicago. Writing about this activity in the January 1965 issue of the *American Mathematical Monthly,* Robert B. Davis makes this significant statement: ". . . the more sophisticated Project work of the past six years has been done primarily with bright students in culturally privileged areas. It comes as a distinct surprise to most of us to discover that *a large part of this 'sophisticated' work is also feasible, and apparently appropriate, on a much wider scale, with culturally deprived urban children.*"

The curriculum proposed by the Cambridge Report moves some college-grade work into the high schools, some high-school grade work into the junior high schools, and some junior-high-school grade work into the elementary schools. Is such a downward movement of the curriculum really psychologically sound? How can it be justified if we accept as valid the theory that the intellectual development of children proceeds through qualitatively distinct stages that occur in a definite sequence? The most influential of these theories today is the theory of the Swiss psychologist, Jean Piaget, who has spent a lifetime studying how children acquire mathematical ideas. Piaget reports that there are four stages in the development of a child's thinking. In the children observed by Piaget and his students, these stages correspond to definite age levels. The sequence of these stages in a child's development is fixed, according to Piaget. During each stage, the child acquires the abilities that prepare him for the next stage. Hence he cannot skip over a stage. However, the preparation for each stage, Piaget says, depends on three principal factors: "maturation of the nervous system, experience acquired in interaction with the physical environment, and the influence of the social milieu." At least two of these factors are subject to our control, since they are cultural rather than genetic. Consequently, while the sequence of the stages is constant, the ages at which they occur is not. Piaget makes this point in these words in the book *The Growth of Logical Thinking from Childhood to Adolescence:* ". . . far from being a source of fully elaborated innate ideas, the maturation of the nervous system can do no more than determine the totality of possibilities and impossibilities at a given stage. A particular social environment remains indispensable for the realization of these possibilities. It follows that their realization can be accelerated or retarded as a function of cultural and educational conditions. This is why the growth of formal thinking as well as the age at which adolescence itself occurs—i.e., the age at which the individual starts to assume adult roles—remain dependent on social as much as and more than on neurological factors."

Thus we see that the kind of acceleration of learning that is proposed by the Cambridge Report is not ruled out as impossible by Piaget's theory of stages in the development of thinking.

In connection with Piaget's theory of stages, it is relevant for us to note again here an observation we made in Chapter 2. According to Piaget, the school child under eleven thinks about objects, but the school child over eleven can think about propositions. While this distinction is basically sound, it should not be interpreted to mean that the child under eleven never uses abstractions, and the child over eleven never has to work with concrete objects and can be introduced to new ideas in abstract form. The first-grade child who figures out that $2 + 3 = 5$ because it is the same as $2 + 2 + 1$ is using abstractions and actually engaging in formal reasoning. On the other hand, no college student really understands what a group is until he has played with many concrete examples. Learning proceeds best from the concrete to the abstract at every age and in every stage.

This observation puts us into a position now to evaluate such proposals as that finite fields be studied in grades three to six. This proposal does not mean that elementary-school children should derive the properties of finite fields deductively from the axioms for a field. It does mean that they should work with specific fields that they can easily construct, namely the clockface number systems in which the circumference of the clockface is divided into a prime number of equal parts. By working with these fields, they can observe the ways in which they differ from other clockface number systems, and can thus discover from concrete examples the difference between a field and a ring that is not a field. They can then appreciate better the significance of the fact that the real number system is a field, but the system of integers is not a field. The procedure will be, as it always should be, to go from the concrete to the abstract.

Thus, it is not in principle more difficult to teach such concepts as that of group, ring, and field than it is to teach the concept of a fraction. I would go beyond this conclusion, however, and argue that the inclusion of such "advanced" concepts in the elementary-school course of study not only does not make it more difficult to teach, but actually makes it easier to teach. The modern ideas of mathematical structure make learning easier because they simplify and unify what the children have to learn. There is an interesting parallel in this respect between the teaching of chemistry and the teaching of mathematics. Chemistry used to be taught as a jumble of disconnected empirical facts, and students rated it as a difficult subject. Now, the advanced ideas of atomic structure are introduced early. As a result, all the formerly disconnected empirical facts fall into place as part of a coherent structure. Now they make sense, and chemistry is becoming an easier subject to learn. Similarly, mathematics was taught in the past as a jumble of disconnected facts. But if we introduce at an early stage the advanced ideas of mathematical structure, all the formerly disconnected mathematical facts will fall into place as part of a coherent whole. They will begin to make sense, and mathematics will be an easier subject to learn.

There is one final argument that I would advance to justify my faith that the kind of curriculum proposed by the Cambridge Report is really teachable. Many parts of this curriculum have already been successfully tested in use in this country and abroad. As Professor Marshall H. Stone says in his critical essay about the report in the April 1965 issue of *The Mathematics Teacher,* ". . . a surprisingly large portion of them [the proposals made in the report] have already been tried out—and with encouraging results—in certain American, European, or Asian schools. And in one country, Denmark, a program essentially as advanced as that proposed by the Cambridge Report (though not nearly so crowded) has already been officially adopted!"

To sum up my argument: I have given four reasons for concluding that the Cambridge Report is not a fantasy, and that it actually points the way to realistic curriculum change:

1. The children can learn more than we think they can.

2. The transition from one stage of learning to the next can be accelerated by a better curriculum and better teaching.

3. The early use of the concepts of mathematical structure accelerates learning by simplifying and unifying the subject matter.

4. Changes like those proposed by the report have already been tried successfully.

Although the goal proposed by the Cambridge Report is realizable, it will not be easy to realize. There are some serious obstacles that will have to be overcome before significant progress toward the goal can be made. The first of these is the low level of mathematical preparation of teachers. As Commissioner Francis Keppel says in his foreword to the Cambridge Report, "It is not only that most teachers will be completely incapable of teaching much of the mathematics set forth in the curricula proposed here; most teachers would be hard put to comprehend it." To overcome this obstacle it will be necessary to launch a major drive to teach all the relevant mathematics to those now teaching and to those who are preparing to teach.

The second major obstacle is the prevalence of some fallacious educational theories which tend to retard learning. I cite four of these that are particularly popular.

One is the I.Q. theory. According to this theory, a child's intelligence is innate and constant, and his I.Q. signifies an upper limit to his ability to learn. As I pointed out in my book *What We Want of Our Schools,* this theory ignores the mounting evidence that a low I.Q. is often the product of cultural deprivation, and that an improved environment can raise a child's learning capacity. Fortunately, teachers and administrators have begun to turn away from the I.Q. theory to the better theory that it is possible and necessary to prepare underprivileged children for school experience through such projects as Operation Headstart. However, while the I.Q. theory is now on the defensive, it has not yet been driven from the field.

A second retarding theory is that a norm of a standardized test represents a satisfactory level of performance. This theory ignores the fact that a norm for a given age is merely a measure of the average performance of children of that age. It indicates what children now do. It does not signify what they may be able to do, or what they ought to do. When we use a norm as a standard of satisfactory performance, we freeze into permanence the educational effects of poverty and disrupted family life, inadequate school curricula, and poor teaching. The only proper attitude toward a norm is to view it as a measure that should be surpassed by any individual or class and should be raised constantly for the country as a whole.

A third retarding theory is that the growth of a child from one stage of learning to another is a process of unfolding from within that cannot be accelerated by educational influences. Proponents of this theory say, correctly, that you should not teach abstract ideas to a child until he is ready for them, but they conclude from this, incorrectly, that you should wait until he is ready. The correct conclusion should be: Don't wait, but help him become ready. As Piaget points out, the transition from one stage of learning to the next can be accelerated or retarded by the kind of teaching we do.

Finally, there is the theory that the child must discover by himself, without teacher guidance, everything that he must learn. Now it is important to give children opportunities to make discoveries on their own level, but, as we saw in Chapter 1, it is also important to recognize the limitations of the discovery method of teaching. Discovery in the classroom must be guided discovery, and often it should be cooperative discovery. As the Cambridge Report says, "Discovery directed by a dialogue between teacher and class, and the direct teacher presentation of material, will be required to attain a reasonable rate of advancement."

To eliminate these false theories that tend to retard learning, it will be necessary to launch a nationwide discussion of educational philosophy for the purpose of reeducating teachers and those who train teachers.

To complete our evaluation of the Cambridge Report we should examine the views about it expressed by Professor Stone in the essay review that I quoted from before. Professor Stone has a "contentious nature," as he himself asserts in the review. He is also a distinguished mathematician who has thought deeply about the problem of improving the mathematics curriculum. This dual character of the reviewer has led to a dual nature of the review. In one part of the review, Professor Stone, the contender, comes out of his corner with both fists swinging, striking not so much at the ideas expressed in the Cambridge Report as at the people who wrote it. He describes the report as "superficial, confused, and shot through with wishful thinking of a shallow kind." He says of the people at the Cambridge Conference that "there were not enough mathematicians distinguished by their thorough knowledge of what is really going on today in pure mathematics." So eager is he to belittle the report and the reporters that he makes contradictory statements about them. For example, he calls the report "ambitious" and displaying "lack of realism," but also denounces it for not being bold enough.

In the other part of his review, Professor Stone, the mathematician and teacher, makes his contribution to the discussion that the Cambridge Conference hoped to initiate. He expresses basic agreement with the program proposed for the elementary schools. For the secondary school he recommends the "introduction of basic concepts of abstract algebra and their application to geometry, through an appeal to groups and vector-systems." "The study of abstract algebra in the secondary school," he says, "should include treatment of the basic structures (groups, rings, fields, modules, vector-systems), of some of the basic concepts (homomorphism, isomorphism, endomorphism), and of at least a few simple theorems (for example, the theorem, very useful for geometrical applications, to the effect that the endomorphisms of a commutative group constitute a ring with unit—and actually one of the most general kind)." For the axiomatic development of geometry, he proposes the use of the axioms for an affine space given by Artin in his book *Geometric Algebra*. The advantage of the

Artin approach, he says, is that it postpones all questions of order until after a line is shown to be equipped with coordinates from an arbitrary skew field. This result then provides the motivation for introducing the further restriction that the base field is the real number system. I am inclined to agree with these positive proposals by Professor Stone, and I hope that there will be further discussion of them.

I urge that all teachers read Professor Stone's review. While they may be repelled by his polemical tone and his ungracious treatment of his colleagues, they should not allow their distaste for his manner to deflect their attention from the substance of what he has to say. He has good ideas that deserve respectful and serious consideration.

Although the Cambridge Report is primarily an attempt to foresee the shape of the mathematics curriculum of the future, it has important implications for what we do in the present. These implications arise in two ways. First, the report is based on certain guiding principles of curriculum development that are valid today as well as tomorrow. Secondly, the only way to attain the curriculum of tomorrow is to prepare for it today. Let us examine briefly these two sets of implications.

The guiding principles that were used in the preparation of the report are principles we all accept. But while we do them honor on ceremonial occasions, we do not always live by them. I list a dozen of them in order to jog our consciences a bit.

1. Beginning with the earliest grades there should be a parallel and integrated development of algebra and geometry.

2. Teach for understanding, not merely for manipulative skill.

3. The first approach to each topic should be intuitive. Use many approaches to illuminate the topic from many sides. Pro-

vide experience in the manipulation of physical objects as the basis for abstract learning.

4. Pay serious attention to the development of suitable problem material. In particular provide the children with problems that give them opportunities to explore and make discoveries that are within their reach.

5. Replace drill for drill's sake by the use of past learnings in new, meaningful situations.

6. Use the spiral approach, in which the same subject arises at different times with increasing degrees of complexity and rigor.

7. Make fuller use of the historical background of a topic to develop an appreciation of how it arose and why it is studied.

8. Many significant mathematical topics can be approached through exciting games, tricks or puzzles. Exploit this recreational aspect of mathematics, especially in the lower grades.

9. Use supplementary pamphlets for individual work by the student who is ready to pursue a topic more broadly and deeply.

10. Show how mathematics is applied in the physical sciences or to other studies of the real world. But keep in mind that many important applications of mathematics are internal, that is, they are applications to mathematics itself. Keep in mind, too, that it is useless to introduce applications whose context the student does not understand.

11. Aim to develop a growing awareness of the nature of logical reasoning. In particular, provide more opportunities for logical inference in grades four to six.

12. In the development of postulational thinking, avoid excessive delicacy and austerity. If proofs are too long and seem to be only laborious ways of arriving at what seems

obvious to the student, the deductive method is not likely to look either attractive or powerful.

The goal proposed by the Cambridge Report can be reached by 1990 only if there is adequate preparation for it today. There are several things that we must do, either individually or collectively as members of institutions, to prepare the schools for teaching the curriculum of the future.

1. Study the Cambridge Report. Know what is in it, and discuss it with your colleagues.

2. Learn more mathematics. If you find mentioned in the report some mathematical ideas that you do not understand, then you know that these are things that you should study.

3. Bring up young teachers and prospective teachers in the spirit of the report. Let its content be their Pablum and its guiding principles their teething rings.

4. Begin to experiment with courses like those that are proposed. Try the new approach at the lowest levels, and extend it upward when you are satisfied with the results.

5. Examine and discuss curricular changes abroad. Import and use what seems to be desirable and workable.

Progress toward the goal of the Cambridge Report will not be easy. But if we all work at trying to get there, we shall surely arrive on time.

Suggested Readings for Chapter 6

Adler, Irving, *A New Look at Arithmetic*. New York, The John Day Company.

———, *The New Mathematics*. New York, The John Day Company.

———, *What We Want of Our Schools*. New York, The John Day Company.

Educational Services, Inc., *Goals for School Mathematics,* Report of the Cambridge Conference on School Mathematics. Boston, Houghton Mifflin Co.

Stone, Marshall H., Review of *Goals for School Mathematics, The Mathematics Teacher,* April 1965.

7.] What Shall We Teach in High-School Geometry?

THE teaching of geometry, dominated by Euclid for two thousand years, has been undergoing searching criticism and significant change during the last sixty years. To understand why, we must consider the question, "What's wrong with Euclid?" A clear answer to this question was given in 1908 by the German mathematician, Felix Klein, and was restated fifty years later by A. E. Meder, one of the leaders of the curriculum reform movement in the United States. Klein pointed out three principal weaknesses in Euclid's approach to geometry:

1. Euclid lacked Archimedes' sense for numerical calculation, his interest in applications, and his heuristic approach.

2. The inadequate arithmetic and algebra of the Greeks compelled Euclid to use cumbersome geometric substitutes, as, for example, in the theory of ratio and proportion.

3. There are defects in the logical structure of Euclid's *Elements.* These include his failure to realize the need for undefined terms; the presence of gaps in the postulate system (the complete absence of axioms of order, for example); and the use of circular reasoning in proofs by superposition.

We may add another reason, too, why Euclid is inadequate for teaching geometry today: Geometry has developed considerably since Euclid's time. There are new approaches to the study of Euclidean geometry, as for example in the coordinate geometry of Descartes. There are also new branches of geometry, such as projective geometry, hyperbolic geometry, and others.

Recent Changes in Some Countries

Mathematics teachers throughout the world, aware of the inadequacies of geometry courses that are based on abbreviated versions of Euclid's *Elements,* have tried to overcome them by introducing a variety of changes into the courses of study. I list ten such changes that have been tried in various combinations in different countries:

1. The use of modified versions of the axioms introduced by David Hilbert to correct the defects in the logical structure of Euclid's *Elements.*

2. The simultaneous development of plane and solid geometry.

3. The early introduction of metric ideas, such as length of segments, angle measure, and area of plane figures.

4. Reliance on the properties of the real number system, as proposed by Birkhoff.

5. The introduction of coordinate geometry.

6. The use of vector methods.

7. The use of those transformations of the plane, called *isometries,* that leave the distance between points unchanged.

8. The inclusion of some non-Euclidean geometry.

9. The development of Euclidean space as a vector space with an inner product, as proposed by Dieudonné.

10. The development of the Euclidean plane as a coordinatized affine plane with the real number system used as the set of coordinates on a line, and with a perpendicularity relation introduced in the plane.

Changes in the United States

In the United States, several different new tenth-grade courses in geometry have been written, and are being used experimentally in schools throughout the country. The best known of these are the two courses called "Geometry" and "Geometry with Coordinates," written by the School Mathematics Study Group (SMSG). The new geometry courses in the United States are based chiefly on the first five changes listed in the preceding paragraph, using them in varying proportions. One course of study, developed by the University of Illinois Committee for School Mathematics, emphasizes change No. 9, the development of Euclidean space as a vector space with an inner product. Another course, developed by the Wesleyan University project, is organized around change No. 10, the development of the Euclidean plane as a coordinatized affine plane with the real number system used as the set of coordinates on a line, and with a perpendicularity relation introduced in the plane.

There is only one feature of the SMSG courses that I shall call attention to here to prepare the way for some references to it later in this chapter. In the traditional geometry course that preceded those written by SMSG, the central topic of the first half-year was that of *congruent triangles*. This topic is still the core of the first half-year in the SMSG courses. However, it is delayed for many weeks while attention is given to some preliminary topics such as the order and separation properties of the plane. For example, in the SMSG text, *Geometry,* congruent triangles are reached for the first time on page 97, after one-sixth of the book for the year has been completed. In the SMSG text, *Geometry with Coordinates,* congruent triangles are reached for the first time on page 225, after one-fourth of the book for the year has been completed.

So many different changes have been proposed or have been tried that it is impossible to incorporate them all into any one course. This makes it necessary to choose among the changes those that seem to be most promising. Thus, in spite of all the worldwide activity directed toward revising the geometry curriculum, teachers are still faced with the question "What shall we teach in high-school geometry?" In this chapter I undertake to give one possible answer to this question.

An answer to the question "What shall we teach in high-school geometry?" must depend on our understanding of the nature of geometry, and on our conception of the goals we try to reach through teaching geometry in the high schools. So let us begin with a brief examination of the nature of geometry and the goals we seek when we teach it.

The Nature of Geometry

I call attention to four significant features of geometry as we know it today.

1. *Geometry is a mathematical model of physical space.* That is, the mathematical entities *point, line, plane, angle,* etc. are idealizations of actual physical points, lines, planes, angles, and so on, and the relations that hold among the mathematical entities approximate very closely the observed relations among their physical counterparts. In the past it was thought that the space described in the geometry of Euclid

was the only adequate mathematical model of physical space. However, we know now that there are other rival spaces that are just as good as mathematical models of physical space. If we assume that physical space is a Riemannian space with constant curvature, then Euclidean space is merely one of three possible models: If physical space has zero curvature, then Euclidean space is the appropriate model; if physical space has positive curvature, then the elliptic space of Riemann is the appropriate model; if physical space has negative curvature, then the hyperbolic space of Gauss, Bolyai and Lobatschewsky is the appropriate model.

2. *Each of these three spaces is constructed by means of an axiomatic system.* That is, the study of each begins with certain undefined terms and with certain assumptions about them known as *axioms*. Then, by deduction from these axioms, various *theorems* are proved. Some of the axioms that describe Euclidean space are also axioms for elliptic space and for hyperbolic space. However, at least one axiom for Euclidean space (the parallel postulate) is different from its elliptic and hyperbolic counterparts.

3. Following the fruitful idea expressed by Felix Klein in his Erlangen Program of 1872, we *now understand a geometry to be the study of those properties of the configurations in a space that remain unchanged when the space is subjected to a group of transformations.* From this point of view, the study of congruent figures in Euclidean plane geometry is part of the study of the geometry associated with the group of *isometries* of the plane, where an isometry is a transformation of the plane that preserves the distances between points.

4. *Geometry is intimately related to algebra.* Ever since Descartes and Fermat invented analytic geometry, we know that the concepts of geometry can be defined in purely al-

gebraic terms. Thus a point in a Euclidean plane can be defined as an ordered pair (x, y) of real numbers, a line in the plane can be defined to be the set of points satisfying an equation of the form $ax + by = c$, and so on. For this reason, some people have concluded that geometry is a branch of algebra. We now know that the procedure can be reversed: such a basic algebraic structure as a *field* can be defined in purely geometric terms. Thus, in an affine plane, it is possible to use certain geometric constructions to define addition and multiplication of the points on a line, and then to show that, with these operations of addition and multiplication, the points on a line constitute a field. In fact, the commutativity of multiplication turns out to be a consequence of Pappus' theorem. Consequently we may conclude with equal validity that algebra is a branch of geometry. Because of this relationship of mutual inclusion, it is now clear that algebra and geometry study essentially the same subject matter, but approach them from different viewpoints and with different methods.

Goals of High-School Geometry

I call attention to five significant goals we should try to attain when we teach geometry in high school.

1. Exploration of relationships among geometric facts previously learned.

2. Introduction to the role of transformations of space in the study of geometry.

3. Mastery of a variety of techniques.

4. Development of critical thinking.

5. Development of an understanding of the nature of a mathematical model.

Let us examine each of these goals separately and see what

changes in the geometry course of study may be necessary to bring us closer to the realization of these goals.

Exploring relationships

Goal 1 is the exploration of relationships among geometric facts previously learned. Traditionally, this has been the principal goal of tenth-grade geometry. Students enter the tenth grade with a fair amount of knowledge of scattered geometric "facts" that they had acquired in earlier grades. In the tenth grade they learn for the first time that these "facts" are not all independent, but that some of them can be derived by deductive reasoning from others. They learn this when they see plane geometry developed as a deductive system built on a set of axioms.

There are many good reasons for stressing axiomatic-deductive reasoning in tenth-grade geometry. First, it is an important type of reasoning that all people should learn to appreciate. Secondly, tenth-grade students are ready for this type of reasoning. Thirdly, geometry is the ideal subject in which to display axiomatic-deductive reasoning, because (*a*) it has been completely axiomatized, (*b*) it is intrinsically interesting because it relates directly to the students intuitive experience with physical space, and (*c*) it is not entangled with the biases and emotions that impede objective thinking in other subjects.

However, the amount of stress given to deductive reasoning in the tenth grade should be determined by the actual need for it. Unfortunately, during the last decade there has been a tendency to stress deductive reasoning more and more while the need for it has actually become less and less. We have increased the stress on deductive reasoning as a result of filling the gaps in Euclid's system of axioms. We have introduced axioms of order and then derived by deduction many propositions that were merely assumed before. As a result, in the SMSG courses, from one-sixth to one-fourth of a year is devoted to deductive reasoning about the order and separation properties of the plane.

At the same time, the need for stressing deductive reasoning has been diminishing. In the past, a student had his first experience with careful deductive reasoning in his tenth-grade geometry class. This is no longer true. As a result of the changes in the mathematics curriculum during the last decade, the students have experience with deductive proofs in ninth-grade algebra, and even in seventh- and eighth-grade arithmetic. Consequently, deductive reasoning doesn't need all the attention that we now give it in the tenth grade.

By not overstressing deductive reasoning in the tenth grade, we can save time and make room for worthwhile additions to the tenth-grade curriculum. I would make these two suggestions for saving time:

1. Take up the order and separation properties of the plane only briefly and intuitively. Display the axioms of order, and indicate that the order and separation theorems can be proved, but do not bother proving them. The proofs are generally not appreciated by the students anyhow, because they find it hard to see the need for proving what seems intuitively obvious.

2. Speed up the treatment of the area sequence in which we start with the formula for the area of a rectangle and then derive in succession the formulas for the area of a parallelogram, a triangle and a trapezoid. The students have had experience with this sequence before. In the ninth grade, and perhaps even earlier, these formulas have already been derived informally but rigorously with the help of some simple visual aids. For example, the student has seen that if right triangle ADE is cut off from one side of parallelogram ABCD

and is attached on the other side, the parallelogram is converted into a rectangle with the same base and height. Thus he sees that a parallelogram with given base and height has the same areas as a rectangle that has the same base and

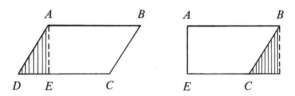

height. Although this proof is informal and easy to grasp, it contains all the essential ideas of a rigorous proof. It is therefore unnecessary to bother writing out a formal proof of this theorem in the tenth grade. A formal proof in this instance adds nothing to the student's understanding, and degenerates into a dull drill routine.

Transformations

Goal 2 is an introduction to the role of transformations of space in the study of geometry. To achieve this goal it is necessary to include in tenth-grade geometry the study of isometries of the plane. One way of doing this is to give the concept of an isometry a central role, as has been done in the schools of Denmark. It would certainly be worthwhile for some American schools to experiment with this approach, perhaps using as axioms those given in Guggenheimer's book, *Plane Geometry and Its Groups*. Another less drastic way of including the study of isometries is to retain the modified Hilbert axioms that are used in the SMSG courses and introduce a short unit on isometries. The content of such a short unit might be built around the following ideas:

1. Definition of an isometry: An isometry of a plane is a

one-to-one mapping of the plane onto itself that preserves distances. It is a "rigid motion" of the plane.

2. Isometries can be multiplied. The product ST of two rigid motions S and T is the single rigid motion that produces the same effect as the motions S and T carried out in succession. With respect to this multiplication operation, the isometries of the plane form a group.

3. The principle of the rigidity of the plane. This principle can be expressed very simply in terms of the concept of a *flag-shaped configuration* obtained in the following way. Let *P* be a point in the plane, and let *m* be a ray that has *P* as vertex. The line of which *m* is a half-line divides the plane into two half-planes. Let *S* be one of these half-planes. In the diagram below, the shading indicates the position of the half-

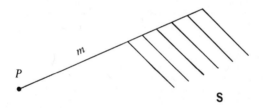

plane *S*. Because the shaded portion of the diagram suggests a flag attached to the ray *m* as flagpole, I call the configuration (*P*, *m*, *S*) determined by the point *P*, the ray *m*, and the half-plane *S* a *flag-shaped configuration*. Let (*P*, *m*, *S*) and (*P'*, *m'*, *S'*) be two such flag-shaped configurations in the plane. Then the principle of the rigidity of the plane is that there is one and only one isometry that moves the flag-shaped configuration (*P*, *m*, *S*) into coincidence with the flag-shaped configuration (*P'*, *m'*, *S'*); that is, that makes *P* fall on *P'*, *m* fall on *m'*, and *S* fall on *S'*. This principle seems intuitively obvious, and may be taken as an assumption, although it is not difficult to prove as a theorem on the basis of the Hilbert axioms.

4. The perimeter of a triangle can be traversed in two opposite senses, a clockwise sense, and a counterclockwise sense, as seen from "above" the plane. For example, in triangle ABC below, the clockwise sense takes you from A to C to B, while the counterclockwise sense takes you from A to B to C.

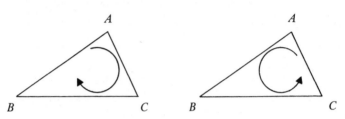

5. Every isometry is either sense-preserving or sense-reversing. *Examples:* (1) A *translation* which moves all the points of the plane the same distance in the same direction is sense-preserving. That is, if it moves A to A', B to B', and C to C',

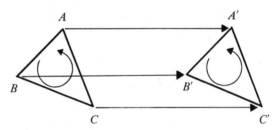

then the sense ABC is the same as the sense $A'B'C'$. (2) A *rotation* of the plane around a point P as center is sense-preserving. In particular, a rotation of $180°$ around P is sense-preserving. Such a $180°$ rotation about P is called a *reflection in P*, and is denoted by R_P. It has the property that if it moves a point A to A', then P is the midpoint of the segment AA'. (3) A *reflection in a line m*, or a *line reflection in m*, denoted

Reflection in a Point P   *Reflection in a Line m*

by R_m, which moves each point A to a point A' on the other side of m so that m is the perpendicular bisector of the segment AA', is sense-reversing. Thus, in the diagram below, the reflection in m, which moves A to A', B to B', and C to C',

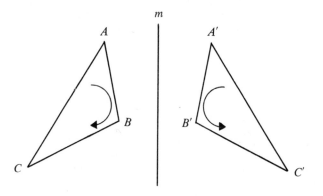

changes the clockwise sense ABC to the counterclockwise sense $A'B'C'$. (4) A *glide reflection,* which is the product of a translation parallel to a line m and a reflection in the line m, is sense-reversing.

6. The four examples given above exhaust the list of all possible isometries: Every sense-preserving isometry of the plane is either a translation or a rotation. Every sense-revers-

ing isometry of the plane is either a reflection in a line or a glide reflection.

7. The product of a reflection in a line m and a reflection in a line n is a translation if the lines are parallel, and is a rotation if the lines intersect. In the first case it is a translation through twice the distance from m to n in the direction that is

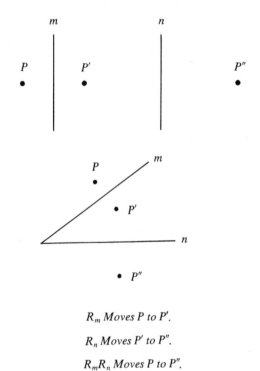

R_m *Moves P to P′.*

R_n *Moves P′ to P″.*

$R_m R_n$ *Moves P to P″.*

perpendicular to them. In the second case it is a rotation through twice the angle from m to n, around the intersection of m and n. In particular, if m is perpendicular to n at O, then the product is a rotation of $180°$ about O, or a reflection in the point O.

8. Every isometry of the plane is a product of at most three line reflections.

9. If we denote by 1 the identity transformation, which leaves every point of the plane fixed, denote by R_a a reflection in the line a, and denote by R_P a reflection in the point P, then $R_a R_a = 1$, and $R_P R_P = 1$.

A variety of techniques

Goal 3 is the mastery of a variety of techniques. We now teach many geometric techniques based on the concepts of congruence, inequality, parallelism, similarity, and area. I would suggest that, in view of the intimate relationship between geometry and algebra, we should pay more attention than we do to algebraic techniques in geometry. I shall discuss briefly the techniques of each of three different kinds of algebra that are useful for the study of geometry: the algebra of coordinates; the algebra of vectors; and the algebra of isometries.

THE ALGEBRA OF COORDINATES, OR CARTESIAN GEOMETRY. The SMSG course called "Geometry with Coordinates" and some other courses include a unit on Cartesian geometry. The usual content of such a unit is limited to three topics: the equation of a line, the formula for the midpoint of a segment, and the formula for the distance between two points. I would suggest the inclusion of one more topic whose simplicity, beauty and usefulness would be appealing to the students: the direction numbers of a line, and their use in tests for parallelism and perpendicularity. Direction numbers of the line whose equation is $ax + by = c$ are any two numbers that are proportional to b and $-a$. If $ax + by = c$ and $a'x + b'y = c'$ are the equations of two given lines, the lines are parallel or coincident if and only if $ab' = a'b$, and they are perpendicular if and only if $aa' + bb' = O$.

THE ALGEBRA OF VECTORS. This subject, usually neglected in most geometry classes, certainly should be brought into the tenth grade. I would suggest inclusion of a unit on vectors, with the following content.

1. The triangle addition rule: $\overrightarrow{AB} + \overrightarrow{BC} = \overrightarrow{AC}$.

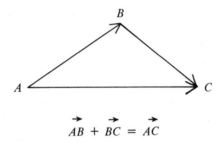

$$\overrightarrow{AB} + \overrightarrow{BC} = \overrightarrow{AC}$$

2. The concept of position vector of a point: Using any arbitrarily chosen origin O, the position vector of a point P is $\overrightarrow{OP}$, and is denoted by **p**.

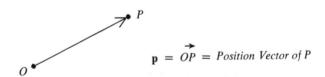

$\mathbf{p} = \overrightarrow{OP} = $ *Position Vector of P*

3. The formula that expresses any vector $\overrightarrow{AB}$ in terms of the position vectors of its endpoints. In the diagram below, where O is the origin, we see that $\overrightarrow{OA} + \overrightarrow{AB} = \overrightarrow{OB}$, or $\mathbf{a} + \overrightarrow{AB} = \mathbf{b}$. Therefore $\overrightarrow{AB} = \mathbf{b} - \mathbf{a}$.

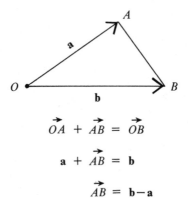

$$\overrightarrow{OA} + \overrightarrow{AB} = \overrightarrow{OB}$$

$$\mathbf{a} + \overrightarrow{AB} = \mathbf{b}$$

$$\overrightarrow{AB} = \mathbf{b} - \mathbf{a}$$

4. The formula that expresses the position vector of the midpoint M of a segment in terms of the position vectors of the endpoints A and B of the segment. In the diagram below we see that $\mathbf{m} = \overrightarrow{OM} = \overrightarrow{OA} + \overrightarrow{AM} = \overrightarrow{OA} + \tfrac{1}{2}\overrightarrow{AB} = \mathbf{a} + \tfrac{1}{2}(\mathbf{b} - \mathbf{a}) = \tfrac{1}{2}(\mathbf{a} + \mathbf{b})$.

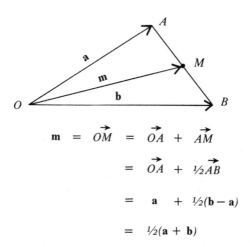

$$
\begin{aligned}
\mathbf{m} = \overrightarrow{OM} &= \overrightarrow{OA} + \overrightarrow{AM} \\
&= \overrightarrow{OA} + \tfrac{1}{2}\overrightarrow{AB} \\
&= \mathbf{a} + \tfrac{1}{2}(\mathbf{b} - \mathbf{a}) \\
&= \tfrac{1}{2}(\mathbf{a} + \mathbf{b})
\end{aligned}
$$

5. Using the midpoint formula for carrying out geometric

proofs. As an example, we show below the proof that the diagonals of a parallelogram bisect each other.

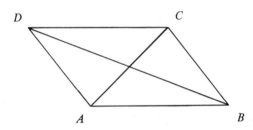

Given: *ABCD* is a parallelogram.
Prove: the midpoint of *BD* = the midpoint of *AC*.

Since *AB* and *DC* are equal and parallel, $\overrightarrow{AB} = \overrightarrow{DC}$, or $\mathbf{b} - \mathbf{a} = \mathbf{c} - \mathbf{d}$. Adding **a** and **d** to both sides of this equation, we get $\mathbf{b} + \mathbf{d} = \mathbf{a} + \mathbf{c}$. Multiplying both sides by ½, we find that $\frac{1}{2}(\mathbf{b} + \mathbf{d}) = \frac{1}{2}(\mathbf{a} + \mathbf{c})$. That is, the position vector of the midpoint of *BD* is equal to the position vector of the midpoint of *AC*. In other words, the midpoint of *BD* and the midpoint of *AC* have the same position.

6. The concept of the inner product (dot product) of two vectors, and its properties. If two vectors **a** and **b** have lengths *l* and *m* respectively, and the angle between them is θ, the inner product $\mathbf{a} \cdot \mathbf{b} = lm \cos \theta$. Its principal properties are these: the commutative law, $\mathbf{a} \cdot \mathbf{b} = \mathbf{b} \cdot \mathbf{a}$; the distributive law, $\mathbf{a} \cdot (\mathbf{b} + \mathbf{c}) = \mathbf{a} \cdot \mathbf{b} + \mathbf{a} \cdot \mathbf{c}$; the test for perpendicularity, if **a** and **b** are not zero, **a** is perpendicular to **b** if and only if $\mathbf{a} \cdot \mathbf{b} = \mathbf{0}$.

7. Using the inner product for carrying out geometric proofs. As an example, we show below the proof that the altitudes of a triangle are concurrent.

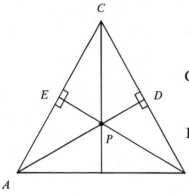

Given: $AD \perp CB$, $BE \perp AC$,
      AD and BE intersect at
      P.

Prove: $CP \perp AB$.

Since $AP \perp BC$, $(\mathbf{p} - \mathbf{a}) \cdot (\mathbf{c} - \mathbf{b}) = 0$. Since $BP \perp CA$, $(\mathbf{p} - \mathbf{b}) \cdot (\mathbf{a} - \mathbf{c}) = 0$. Expanding these two equations via the distributive law, we get

$\mathbf{p} \cdot \mathbf{c} - \mathbf{p} \cdot \mathbf{b} - \mathbf{a} \cdot \mathbf{c} + \mathbf{a} \cdot \mathbf{b} = 0$, and

$-\mathbf{p} \cdot \mathbf{c} + \mathbf{p} \cdot \mathbf{a} + \mathbf{b} \cdot \mathbf{c} - \mathbf{a} \cdot \mathbf{b} = 0$. Adding these two equations, and then factoring, we get $\mathbf{p} \cdot (\mathbf{a} - \mathbf{b}) - \mathbf{c} \cdot (\mathbf{a} - \mathbf{b}) = 0$, and $(\mathbf{p} - \mathbf{c}) \cdot (\mathbf{a} - \mathbf{b}) = 0$. Since $\mathbf{p} - \mathbf{c} \neq 0$, and $\mathbf{a} - \mathbf{b} \neq 0$, this means that $CP \perp BA$.

THE ALGEBRA OF ISOMETRIES. This subject, until now totally ignored by the curriculum revision movement in the United States, has many interesting facets that would appeal to tenth-grade students. Some have already been mentioned on page 138. I shall discuss briefly here one aspect of the subject that opens up the possibility of translating geometric problems into algebraic problems in the group of isometries. If we match every point P in the plane with R_P, the reflection in the point P, we establish a one-to-one correspondence between the set of all points in the plane and the set of all reflections in a point. Similarly, if we match every line a in the plane with R_a, the reflection in the line a, we establish a one-to-one correspondence between the set of all lines in the plane and the set of all reflections in a line. Using these correspondences, it is possible to set up a dictionary for translating geometric statements about points and lines into algebraic statements about reflections in a point and reflections in a line, and vice versa. Part of such a dictionary is shown below. The proof of the validity of the dictionary is given in the book *A New Look at Geometry*. (See the list of suggested readings at the end of the chapter.)

GEOMETRIC STATEMENT	ALGEBRAIC STATEMENT
P is on a.	$R_P R_a = R_a R_P$.
$a \perp b$.	$a \neq b$, and $R_a R_b = R_b R_a$
b is the perpendicular bisector of $\overline{PQ}$.	$R_P R_b = R_b R_Q$.
M is the midpoint of $\overline{AC}$.	$R_A R_M = R_M R_C$.
$\overline{AB} = \overline{DC}$, and $AB \parallel DC$.	$R_A R_B = R_D R_C$.

Using this dictionary provides a way of solving geometric problems by algebraic means. As an example we give the proof of the geometric exercise shown below.

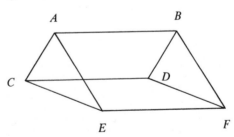

Given: $\overline{AC} = \overline{BD}$, $AC \parallel BD$, $\overline{CE} = \overline{DF}$, $CE \parallel DF$.
Prove: $\overline{AE} = \overline{BF}$, $AE \parallel BF$.

Reading the last line of the dictionary from left to right translates the hypothesis into two algebraic statements as follows: Since $\overline{AC} = \overline{BD}$, and $AC \parallel BD$, $R_A R_C = R_B R_D$. Since $\overline{CE} = \overline{DF}$, and $CE \parallel DF$, $R_C R_E = R_D R_F$. Multiplying these two equations, we get $R_A R_C R_C R_E = R_B R_D R_D R_F$. As we noted on page 143, $R_C R_C = 1$ and $R_D R_D = 1$. Making these substitutions, we get $R_A 1 R_E = R_B 1 R_F$, or $R_A R_E = R_B R_F$. Reading the last line of the dictionary from right to left, we see that this last algebraic statement is equivalent to the geometric statement $\overline{AE} = \overline{BF}$ and $AE \parallel BF$.

Critical thinking

Goal 4 is the development of critical thinking. To be able to move toward this goal, we must take into account the fact that the ability to reason deductively from a set of assumptions does not by itself guarantee the ability to think critically. In fact, if the student knows of only one set of conclusions, deduced from the commonly used assumptions, he can easily fall into the trap of thinking that the conclusions are necessarily true, rather than being merely consequences of the assumptions. Then his deductive reasoning would be encouraging dogmatic thinking rather than critical thinking. Genuinely critical thinking requires that the student appreciate the conditional character of conclusions arrived at by deductive reasoning from a set of assumptions: *The conclusions depend on the assumptions, and if we change the assumptions we may arrive at different conclusions.* An effective way of demonstrating this principle is to show that if we change the axioms of Euclidean geometry to convert them into the axioms of hyperbolic geometry, then some of the conclusions that follow from the axioms are changed. For example, while in Euclidean geometry the sum of the angles of a triangle is 180°, in hyperbolic geometry the sum of the angles of a triangle is less than 180°. For this reason it is desirable to include in tenth-grade geometry a short unit on hyperbolic geometry. A sequence of lessons in hyperbolic geometry leading up to the theorem that in hyperbolic geometry the sum of the angles of a triangle is less than 180° need not take more than two weeks. (See the article by Maiers in the list of suggested readings at the end of the chapter.)

To obtain the axioms of hyperbolic geometry from the Hilbert axioms for Euclidean geometry, we need only replace the Euclidean axiom of parallels that through a point not on a line there is only one line parallel to the given line, by the hyperbolic axiom that through a point not on a line there is more than one line parallel to the given line. All other axioms of Euclidean geometry are also axioms of hyperbolic geometry. All theorems that can be deduced from these axioms alone, without using either of the axioms of parallels, are theorems of both hyperbolic geometry and Euclidean geometry. Bolyai gave the name "absolute geometry" to the set of all axioms and theorems that are common to both Euclidean and hyperbolic geometry. It seems to me that it would make sense for us to start tenth-grade geometry with absolute geometry, then indicate that we have a choice of parallel postulates, and explore the consequences of each choice, pursuing the hyperbolic choice only briefly and dealing with the Euclidean choice more fully. Many of the theorems now studied in the tenth grade are theorems of absolute geometry. They should be identified as such, and should be proved in such a way that it is clear that they do not depend on the axiom of parallels. For example, the AAS theorem "Two triangles are congruent if two angles and the side opposite one of them in one triangle are equal respectively to two angles and the corresponding side in the other triangle" is a theorem of absolute geometry. Unfortunately some textbooks hide this fact by basing the proof of the AAS theorem on the Euclidean theorem that the sum of the angles of a triangle is 180°, thus making it appear that the AAS theorem depends on the axiom of parallels. Incidentally, Euclid did not make this mistake in his *Elements*. He gave a proof that does not depend on the axiom of parallels, so it is valid in both Euclidean geometry and hyperbolic geometry. In this instance we can improve our teaching of geometry by going back to Euclid!

In addition to those theorems of absolute geometry that we already teach, I would suggest the inclusion of two others that are very important both conceptually and historically: the theorem giving the basic properties of a Saccheri quadrilateral, and Legendre's theorem that the sum of the angles of a triangle is less than or equal to two right angles.

Quadrilateral $ABCD$, shown below, is called a Saccheri quadrilateral, if $DA \perp AB$, $CB \perp AB$, and $\overline{DA} = \overline{CB}$. Let H be the midpoint of $\overline{DC}$, and let M be the midpoint of $\overline{AB}$.

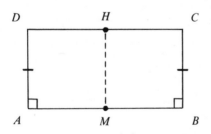

Saccheri Quadrilateral

It is easy to prove that $MH \perp DC$, $MH \perp AB$, and angle $D =$ angle C. Angles D and C are called the *summit* angles of the Saccheri quadrilateral. Three different hypotheses may be considered: (A) the summit angles are acute angles; (B) the summit angles are right angles; (C) the summit angles are obtuse angles. Hypothesis A leads to hyperbolic geometry. Hypothesis B leads to Euclidean geometry. Hypothesis C is inconsistent with absolute geometry, so it must be rejected. (It leads to elliptic geometry only if the axioms of absolute geometry are modified to permit a line to be finite though unbounded, with circular order relations rather than linear order relations.)

It is important for students to see a proof of Legendre's theorem so that they may appreciate the importance of the axiom of Archimedes. A proof is outlined below.

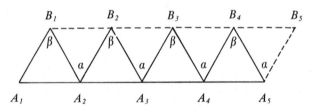

Given: $A_1A_2 = A_2A_3 = \ldots$

$\triangle A_1A_2B_1 \cong \triangle A_2A_3B_2 \cong \ldots$

$\triangle B_1B_2A_2 \cong \triangle B_2B_3A_3 \cong \ldots$

Prove: $\beta \leqq \alpha$.

Suppose $\beta > \alpha$.

Then $A_1A_2 > B_1B_2$, $A_1A_2 - B_1B_2 > O$.

$A_1B_1B_2B_3B_4B_5A_5 > A_1A_5$

$A_1B_1 + 4B_1B_2 + B_5A_5 > 4A_1A_2$

$$2A_1B_1 > 4(A_1A_2 - B_1B_2).$$

Similarly $2A_1B_1 > n(A_1A_2 - B_1B_2)$, for any positive integer n. That is, no multiple of the segment $A_1A_2 - B_1B_2$ exceeds in length the segment $2A_1B_1$. But this is contradicted by the axiom of absolute geometry that is known as the axiom of

Archimedes, which asserts that there is a multiple of any segment, no matter how small the segment may be, that exceeds in length any other segment, no matter how large that segment may be. (Archimedes' axiom says, in effect, that you can travel any large distance by taking small steps, provided that you take enough steps.)

The nature of a mathematical model

Goal 5 is the development of an understanding of the nature of a mathematical model. It can be achieved by exploring with the students the meaning of the fact that Euclidean geometry is a mathematical model of physical space.

Because Euclidean geometry is a model of physical space, we can perform geometry experiments in the classroom and arrive at some propositions by inductive reasoning. This fact is the basis of the "laboratory" method of teaching geometry which has been popular for several decades. Unfortunately, because of some common misconceptions about the nature of inductive and deductive reasoning, teachers using the laboratory method often cultivate confusion rather than understanding.

Some teachers incorrectly characterize inductive reasoning as a process of proving a general rule by examining particular cases. For example, this is the conception of inductive reasoning given on page 5 of the SMSG textbook, *Geometry with Coordinates*. However, this view is clearly wrong, because particular cases can prove a rule only if every possible case, without exception, has been examined and has been shown to conform to the rule. But, in the typical geometry experiment, the number of possible cases is infinite, so it is impossible to examine them all. Suppose, for example, we try to "prove" by experiment that the base angles of an isosceles triangle are equal. We may draw a million isosceles triangles of a variety of sizes and shapes, and, by measuring their base angles, find that in each case the base angles are approximately equal. But this tells us nothing about the infinitely many isosceles triangles that we have not drawn. Hence we cannot conclude that the base angles are equal in *every* isosceles triangle. What, then, is the logical relationship between the observations made in this experiment and the generalization that the base angles of an isosceles triangle are equal? The correct answer to this question is that *while the observations do not prove the generalization, the generalization explains the observations*. That is, if it is true that the base angles of every isosceles triangle are equal, then that would explain why in so many particular cases the measured base angles turn out to be approximately equal, with any difference between the measures smaller than the possible errors of measurement.

Some teachers correctly point out that particular cases do not prove a general rule, and then incorrectly conclude from this fact that deduction is superior to induction. They argue that induction may establish only that a theorem is true for the observed cases, but a deductive proof of the theorem establishes that it is true for all cases. Such an argument shows a complete misunderstanding of the nature of deductive reasoning. Actually a deductive proof of a theorem doesn't show it to be true for any cases at all. All it shows is that the theorem is a consequence of the axioms. Hence the truth of the theorem is conditional. The theorem is true if the axioms are true.

What, then, is the nature of deductive reasoning and of inductive reasoning, and what is the relationship between them?

Deductive reasoning is not concerned with truth. It is concerned with implications. In deductive reasoning, we start with premises, and show that they imply certain conclusions.

In inductive reasoning, we start with a set of statements, and we look for premises from which these statements can be deduced as conclusions. We do not then assert the truth of these premises. We merely say that the given statements make it look *as if* the premises are true. Sometimes there may be a choice of different sets of premises that may imply the same conclusions.

Thus inductive reasoning is the opposite of deductive reasoning in this sense: in deductive reasoning we proceed from premises to conclusions; in inductive reasoning we work backward from conclusions to premises. In both cases, the premises imply the conclusions, but the conclusions do not necessarily imply the premises. Notice that while inductive reasoning is the opposite of deductive reasoning, inductive reasoning includes deductive reasoning, since, in inductive reasoning, we look for premises from which we can *deduce* the desired conclusions.

Students who understand the nature of deductive reasoning and of inductive reasoning can be led to understand what it means when we say that Euclidean geometry is a mathematical model of physical space. Euclidean geometry is a mathematical model of physical space because it has these four characteristics:

1. Each undefined term and each defined term in Euclidean geometry is associated with some physical object. Thus the word *line* may be associated with an axis of rotation of a rigid body.

2. The axioms of Euclidean geometry express certain assumed relationships of these undefined terms.

3. The theorems of Euclidean geometry are deductions from these axioms that express other relationships among the undefined terms and/or the defined terms.

4. If the axioms and theorems of Euclidean geometry are interpreted to be assertions about the physical objects associated with its terms, then, to the extent that these assertions have been tested by experiment, they have been found to be approximately true.

Thus, in order to be able to achieve goal 5, it is necessary that we first eliminate the common misconceptions about the nature of inductive and deductive reasoning.

What Shall We Teach?

I have answered the question "What shall we teach in high-school geometry?" by suggesting some specific changes in the courses now being taught. I have proposed:

1. Saving time by using a less deductive treatment of the order and separation properties of the plane and a less formal treatment of the area sequence.

2. Introducing a unit on isometries of the plane.

3. Paying more attention to algebraic techniques.

4. Introducing a unit on hyperbolic geometry.

5. Eliminating misconceptions about the nature of inductive and deductive reasoning. Change 5 is essential. Changes 2, 3 and 4 are additions that are desirable. Change 1 is a deletion that will make it possible for one or more of these additions to be made.

Suggested Readings for Chapter 7

Adler, Irving, *A New Look at Geometry*. New York, The John Day Company.

Blumenthal, Leonard M., *A Modern View of Geometry*. San Francisco, W. H. Freeman & Co.

Brand, Louis, *Vector and Tensor Analysis* (Chapter I). New York, John Wiley & Sons.

Coxeter, H. S. M., *Introduction to Geometry*. New York, John Wiley & Sons.

Guggenheimer, Heinrich W., *Plane Geometry and Its Groups*. San Francisco, Holden-Day.

Jones, Burton W., "Reflections and Rotations." *The Mathematics Teacher,* October 1961.

Kemeny, John G., "Report to the International Congress of Mathematicians." *The Mathematics Teacher,* February 1963.

Klein, Felix, *Elementary Mathematics from an Advanced Standpoint* (Geometry, pp. 188–208). New York, Dover.

Macdonald, I. D., "Abstract Algebra from Axiomatic Geometry." *The Mathematics Teacher,* February 1966.

Maiers, Wesley W., "Introduction to non-Euclidean Geometry." *The Mathematics Teacher,* November 1964.

Meder, Albert E., Jr., "What Is Wrong with Euclid?" *The Mathematics Teacher,* December 1958.

Modenov, P. S. and Parkhomenko, A. S., *Geometric Transformations,* Vol. I. New York, Academic Press.

School Mathematics Study Group, *Teachers Commentary, Geometry.* New Haven, Yale University Press.

What Shall We Teach in High-School Geometry?

Troyer, Robert J., "An Approach to Vector Geometry." *The Mathematics Teacher,* May 1963.

Wolfe, Harold E., *Non-Euclidean Geometry.* New York, Dryden Press.

Yaglom, I. M., *Geometric Transformations.* New York, Random House.

8.] The Group Concept in the Curriculum of the Future

THE Cambridge Conference that met in 1963 tried to picture what the precollege mathematics curriculum of the future should be like to meet the growing mathematical needs of contemporary society. The report of the conference forecast that in the future we would have to teach in nine years what we now teach in twelve. To make this feat possible, the conference recommended a reorganization of the curriculum around some central mathematical ideas, with more emphasis on meaning and less emphasis on rote drill. One of the central ideas that occurs often in the courses recommended by the conference for grades seven through ten is that of a *group*. To prepare children for these secondary-level courses of the future, it is necessary that this concept receive more attention in the elementary grades than it does now. We should begin immediately to experiment with ways of developing the concept of a group, starting in the first grade with informal experiences with specific groups, and culminating at about the sixth grade in an elementary study of groups as algebraic structures satisfying a particular set of axioms.

The Group Concept in the Curriculum of the Future

In 1959, the Commission on Mathematics of the College Entrance Examination Board had recommended that the concepts of *set, relation* and *function* be used as unifying ideas around which the curriculum should be reconstructed. These ideas now constitute a kind of trivium of mathematical education. The spirit of the Cambridge Conference Report requires that this trivium be expanded to a quadrivium by adding the group concept as another important unifying idea. To examine this requirement and its implications, let us proceed by answering three questions: *What? Why?* and *How?* We shall consider *what* a group is; *why* the concept of a group is so important that it should be used as a central idea in the mathematics curriculum; and *how* the concept can be built up gradually through a graded series of activities suited to the physical and intellectual maturity of the child.

What is a group? Roughly, we may say that a group is a set in which there is an operation that is associative and reversible. If we call the operation "multiplication" and use the usual notation for representing it, we may say more specifically that a group is a set S and a multiplication operation in S with these four properties: (1) If a and b are members of S, then the product ab is a member of S. This is called the closure property. (2) If a, b and c are members of S, then $(ab)c = a(bc)$. This is called the associative property. (3) S contains a member called i with the property that, for every member a in S, $ia = ai = a$. (4) For every member a in S there is another member b with the property $ab = ba = i$. A consequence of this last property is the fact that the multiplication operation is reversible, that is, that division by any member of S is always possible.

The element i mentioned in property No. 3 is called the identity element of the group. It is sometimes represented by the symbol 1. For each element a in S, the element b mentioned in property No. 4 is called the inverse of a and is sometimes represented by the symbol a^{-1}.

In some groups, but not all, the multiplication operation also has the commutative property, that, if a and b are members of S, then $ab = ba$. A group with this property is called a commutative group. In a commutative group, the group operation is sometimes called "addition" instead of "multiplication" and is represented by the symbol $+$. If this additive notation is used, then the identity element is represented by the symbol 0 and is called *zero,* and the inverse of a is represented by the symbol $-a$.

The concept of a group is more complex than the concepts of set, relation or function. Moreover, a group is only one of several important algebraic structures that occur in the mathematics courses of the elementary- and secondary-school grades. The others are the structures called rings, fields and vector spaces. Then why should we single out the complex concept of a group for special emphasis alongside the simpler and more fundamental concepts of set, relation and function? There are four principal reasons why the concept of a group deserves this special distinction.

1. A principal goal of teaching mathematics in the elementary and secondary schools is the development of an understanding of the nature and uses of certain number fields, namely the field of rational numbers, the field of real numbers, and the field of complex numbers. A field is a set in which two operations, addition and multiplication, are defined, subject to certain axioms. So a field has a twofold structure: it has an additive structure and a multiplicative structure. The structure of a field may be represented by the following diagram:

Structure of a Field F

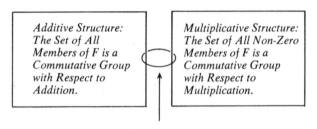

Additive Structure: The Set of All Members of F is a Commutative Group with Respect to Addition.

Multiplicative Structure: The Set of All Non-Zero Members of F is a Commutative Group with Respect to Multiplication.

Distributive Law:
$$a(b+c)=ab+ac$$

Thus we see that a field consists of two group structures linked by the distributive law. So, in order to understand the nature of a number field, it is necessary to understand the nature of a group.

Similarly, the concept of a group underlies the other algebraic structures, rings and vector spaces, that are encountered in the mathematics courses in the elementary- and secondary-school grades. The principal examples of a ring with which children have some experience in the upper grades are the ring of integers and the ring of polynomials with real coefficients. The principal examples of a vector space with which they have some experience are the set of all displacements in space and the set of all possible forces acting at a point.

A ring, like a field, has an additive structure and a multiplicative structure linked by a distributive law. The concept of a group is part of the concept of a ring because the additive structure of a ring is a group. For example, the set of all integers is a group with respect to addition. Similarly, the set of all polynomials in one variable with real coefficients is a group with respect to addition.

A vector space has an additive structure and an associated

field structure, the field of scalars. The two structures are linked by scalar multiplication subject to certain axioms. The concept of a group is part of the concept of a vector space because the additive structure of a vector space is a commutative group, and the associated scalar field contains, as we have seen, two group structures. So a vector space is a structure compounded out of three groups. Thus, to understand the nature of either a ring or a vector space, it is necessary to understand the nature of a group.

2. Another principal goal of teaching mathematics in the elementary and secondary schools is to introduce children to the geometry of Euclidean space. If we examine the meaning of the terms *Euclidean space* and *geometry* we find more reasons why the concept of a group is important. One way of defining a Euclidean space is to say that it is a vector space associated with the field of real numbers with a kind of product called an inner product defined for any two vectors. This definition of Euclidean space is the basis of one of the tenth-grade courses proposed by the Cambridge Conference. As we have already seen, the concept of a group is intrinsic to the concept of a vector space. Hence it is intrinsic to the concept of Euclidean space.

The meaning of the term geometry generally accepted today is that given to it by Felix Klein in his Erlangen Program of 1872. A geometry is the study of those properties of a space that are invariant with respect to a particular group of transformations of the space. This conception of geometry underlies the ninth-grade courses proposed by the Cambridge Conference. Each different group of transformations of a space determines a different geometry of the space. Thus the concept of a group is intrinsic to the concept of a geometry. So we see that it is necessary to learn about groups in order to be able to study Euclidean geometry from the point of view that may be used in the ninth- and tenth-grade courses of the future.

3. A third principal goal of teaching mathematics in the elementary and secondary schools is to equip children with the mathematical concepts and skills that will be useful to them as tools for exploring and controlling their environment. A significant feature of their environment, both natural and man-made, is the widespread occurrence of symmetry. Because symmetry occurs so often in nature, the study of symmetry is part of the study of science. Because symmetry is used so often in painting, sculpture, architecture, and every type of design, the study of symmetry is part of the study of art. The mathematical tool for studying symmetry is the group. So groups are important because of their uses in art and science.

4. A fourth principal goal of teaching mathematics in the elementary and secondary schools is to develop in children the ability to think logically. According to Piaget, a child's mental growth proceeds through a succession of four stages. The child advances from the second to the third stage when he begins to use in his thinking the mental acts that Piaget calls *operations*. Piaget defines an operation as "an action which can return to its starting point, and which can be integrated with other actions also possessing this feature of reversibility." Because operations are reversible and can be combined, a system of operations has the structure of a mathematical group, with a law of composition of elements, an identity element, an inverse for every element, and an associative law. The child makes the transition from the preoperational stage of thinking to the next higher stage when his mental acts that used to be isolated and unrelated are

finally organized into such grouplike structures. The grouplike structure of the child's thinking is a distillation from his experience. It is a reflection in his mind of the group structures that he has encountered. So, if Piaget's theory of intellectual growth is valid, experience with groups is important because it helps to develop the ability to think logically.

Here then are the reasons why the group concept deserves special attention: Groups are important for understanding the structures encountered in arithmetic and algebra, for understanding the geometry of Euclidean space, for dealing with symmetry in art and nature, and for learning to reason effectively.

Now let us consider the question of how we should modify the mathematics curriculum so that, starting with the first grade, it contributes to and takes advantage of an ever deepening understanding of groups and their uses. Let me begin by saying that we should not do it by trying to inject into the elementary-school curriculum the formal study of a group as an axiomatic system. In the first place, most children below the sixth grade are not yet ready for the hypothetical reasoning required to deduce theorems from axioms. In the second place, the study of groups does not begin with the concept of a group. It begins with experience with concrete groups. The concept of a group emerges later as a generalization from this experience. Therefore, to give groups their proper place in the curriculum, I propose that these steps be taken:

1. Provide early experience in the elementary grades with a variety of specific groups.

2. Develop early the concepts and skills that are necessary for studying and using groups.

3. Provide early experience with certain particular groups that are important for later study and applications.

4. Make the transition to formal study of abstract groups as soon as the pupil is prepared for it, at about the sixth grade.

5. Having built up the group concept in this way in grades one to six, use it explicitly at the appropriate places in the curriculum for grades seven through ten.

Let us now consider each of these five steps in some detail.

Providing experience with specific groups

In the traditional mathematics curriculum, the first group that the children had any experience with was the multiplicative group of positive rational numbers. They encountered it for the first time in the sixth grade, when they mastered the multiplication of fractions. The next group that they became acquainted with was the additive group of integers. They met this group in the ninth grade when they first became acquainted with negative numbers. This experience with groups was too little and too late.

The School Mathematics Study Group (SMSG) improved the situation somewhat by moving the additive group of integers down to the sixth grade, by introducing the clockface or modular number systems in the seventh grade, and by examining in the eighth grade the field structures of the rational number system and the real number system. Through the clockface number systems the children became acquainted with many finite groups, and in the number systems modulo a prime they even met some finite fields. By seeing side by side the rational number field, the real number field, and the finite clockface fields, they could begin to appreciate that a field consists of two group structures linked by the distributive law.

But this improvement introduced by SMSG is not enough. We should begin to expose the child to groups as early as the first grade. Here are some of the ways in which this can be done.

1. We can introduce the additive group of integers in the first grade, by means of the number line, as recommended by the Cambridge Conference. Addition can be done by combining motions on the line. Thus to add $2 + (-5)$, start at 0, move two units to the right, and then move five units to the left. (See the diagram on page 105.)

The conference also suggests that first-grade equipment include number line rulers, on which zero is in the middle rather than at one end. Two such rulers held side by side make a slide rule for the addition of integers. The diagram on page 106 shows how the slide rule is used to find the sum $2 + (-5)$.

We might also experiment with the use of colored blocks, beads or checkers to represent integers. For example, a white checker may represent 1, and a black checker may represent -1. Then two white checkers stand for 2, and five black checkers stand for -5. Since $1 + (-1) = 0$, as shown on the number line, then a white checker combined with a black checker stand for 0. To find the sum of 2 and -5, the child would unite a set of two white checkers with a set of five black checkers, and then remove from the set all the zero combinations of one white checker and one black checker that can be

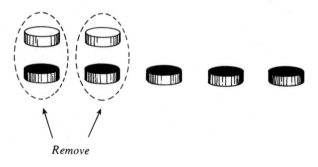

Remove

formed. After this has been done, only three black checkers are left, showing that $2 + (-5) = -3$.

To provide a classroom situation in which integers may be added, we can play games in which there are both credits and penalties. Then we can represent the credits by positive integers and the penalties by negative integers.

The concept of positive and negative integer, once developed, should be kept alive from grade to grade by constant use. A device that can be used after the children have learned about place value and have developed some facility with the fundamental operations is the *negative digit,* proposed by a recent writing workshop of the Cambridge Conference. Let $\hat{1}, \hat{2}, \ldots, \hat{9}$ stand for $-1, -2, \ldots, -9$. Then $1\hat{1}$ stands for $10 + (-1) = 9$, $1\hat{2}$ stands for $10 + (-2) = 8$, etc. Exercises might include changing from ordinary numerals to numerals using negative digits, and vice versa, adding numerals with negative digits, and then checking by using ordinary numerals.

2. We can introduce a group of motions in the second grade by playing a modified version of the game "Simon Says," as follows. The leader may give any one of six commands, *left face, right face, about face, Simon says left face, Simon says right face,* and *Simon says about face.* The command is to be obeyed only when it begins with the words "Simon says." Any child who moves when he is not supposed to is eliminated from the game. The last remaining player is the winner. After the children know the game well, play a new version of it in which each command given consists of two commands from the old game given in succession. For example, *Simon says left face and Simon says left face,* or *Simon says left face and Simon says right face, or left face and Simon says left face.* After responding correctly, the chil-

dren will be able to determine what single command has the same effect as the two commands that are combined when they are given in succession. In later grades, the children will be able to use symbols to represent the effect of each command. For example, they may use L for *Simon says left face;* R for *Simon says right face;* A for *Simon says about face;* and I for a command that does not begin with "Simon says." The children will then discover that LL = A, IL = L, AA = I, etc. If these results are recorded in a multiplication table in which there are four rows labeled I, L, R, and A respectively, and four columns labeled I, L, R and A respectively, the result will be a typical group table, displaying all the characteristic features of a group.

	I	*L*	*R*	*A*
I	*I*	*L*	*R*	*A*
L	*L*	*A*	*I*	*R*
R	*R*	*I*	*A*	*L*
A	*A*	*R*	*L*	*I*

3. We can introduce more groups of motions in the third and higher grades by having the children manipulate such plane figures as a square, a rectangle, and an equilateral triangle in order to discover and combine their symmetries. A symmetry of a plane figure is a motion which brings it into coincidence with itself. For example, a square may be brought into coincidence with itself by being given a quarter turn, a half turn, a three-quarter turn, or a full turn clockwise, or by being flipped over, using as axis of rotation either diagonal or either line joining the midpoints of opposite sides. Motions

that have the same effect are considered to be equal. Two motions combined by performing them in succession turn out to have the same effect as one of the original eight motions. With this operation of combining motions, the symmetries of a square form a group. The children can discover the products in this group by themselves and can then construct the multiplication table for the group. They can observe in the table that if I stands for a full turn, and X stands for any one of the symmetries of a square then $IX = XI = X$. That is, I is the identity element of the group. They can observe, too, that for every member X of the set of symmetries of a square, there is another member Y with the property that $XY = YX = I$. That is, every symmetry of a square has an inverse.

A unit on the symmetries of plane figures was prepared by a Cambridge Conference workshop and tried out with second- and third-grade classes. The lesson was successful in the third grade. However, it failed in the second grade, chiefly because the children had great difficulty in flipping over the figures. The trial lesson showed, too, that work with a square was easier than work with an equilateral triangle, because the children were more familiar with the fractions ¼, ½ and ¾ than they were with ⅓ and ⅔.

An informal introduction to subgroups of a group can be provided in the fourth grade through an examination of the symmetries of a letter of the alphabet drawn inside a square, as in these diagrams:

The figures examined for symmetry may be extended to include natural objects, such as the flower of a geranium or of a myrtle, and simple finite ornamental designs such as the swastika.

Having had experiences like these in the third and fourth grades, the children will be prepared to study in the fifth grade the more difficult symmetries of infinite repeating border ornaments. There are only seven basic types of infinite repeating border ornaments, each characterized by a particular group of symmetries. The seven types are shown in this diagram.

The symmetries of a band ornament can be made visible as actual motions if two copies of the ornament are printed on transparent acetate sheets. Then one sheet can be moved over the other to see which motions leave the ornament unchanged. Activities for the children might include identifying all the symmetries for a given ornament; finding the product of two symmetries; identifying the type of a given ornament; and making up an ornament of a given type.

4. Groups of transformations of finite sets can probably be introduced in the fourth or fifth grades. A transformation of a finite set is a matching of the set with itself, in which each member of the set is matched with one and only one member of the set. The matching may be displayed concretely by moving something from each member of the set to the member that it is matched with. For example, consider the set of three numbered squares shown in the diagram. To display a trans-

formation of this set of squares, put a checker on each square. Then move each checker from the square it occupies to another square, which may perhaps be the same one. The moves can be recorded in tables like this:

i:	p:	q:
1 ⟶ 1	1 ⟶ 1	1 ⟶ 3
2 ⟶ 2	2 ⟶ 3	2 ⟶ 2
3 ⟶ 3	3 ⟶ 2	3 ⟶ 1

r:	s:	t:
1 ⟶ 2	1 ⟶ 2	1 ⟶ 3
2 ⟶ 1	2 ⟶ 3	2 ⟶ 1
3 ⟶ 3	3 ⟶ 1	3 ⟶ 2

The last table, for example, describes the transformation t in which the checker on the 1 square moves to the 3 square, the checker on the 2 square moves to the 1 square, and the checker on the 3 square moves to the 2 square.

Two transformations can be combined by performing them in succession and then seeing which single transformation has the same effect. The next diagram shows that if transformation t is followed by transformation p, the effect is that the checker that starts on the 1 square ends on the 2 square, the checker that starts on the 2 square ends on the 1 square, and the checker that starts on the 3 square ends on the 3 square. The

```
        t:              p:
1 ————————→ 3 ————————→ 2
2 ————————→ 1 ————————→ 1
3 ————————→ 2 ————————→ 3
```

same effect is produced by transformation r. This shows that tp = r. The set of all possible transformations of a given set of objects is a group with respect to the operation of combining transformations. The children can easily discover the multiplication table for this group.

5. The concept of a group of residue classes modulo a counting number greater than 1 can probably be introduced in the sixth grade. However, something can be done in each of the lower grades to build up gradually the component ideas that make up this important concept. To show how this might be done, I list a sequence of steps that may be taken, starting in grade one, and ending in grade six, to develop a deeper and deeper insight into the relationship between the residue classes modulo two. These residue classes are the set of even numbers and the set of odd numbers.

Step 1. Using blocks, find out which numbers can be represented by a set of blocks arranged in two equal rows of blocks. Which numbers can be represented by a set arranged in two rows in which one row has one more block than the other? This activity establishes the concept of odd and even.

Step 2. Count by twos, starting with 1. Count by twos, starting with 2.

Step 3. When preparing to play a team game, count off to choose the teams. The odd-numbered pupils will be in one team, and the even-numbered pupils will be in the other team. This provides a convenient excuse for using the concepts of odd and even.

Step 4. Solve puzzles like these: Find two even numbers whose sum is 11. Find two odd numbers whose sum is 11.

Step 5. In the course of struggling with step 4, the children will observe that an even number + an even number = an even number; an even number + an odd number = an odd number; an odd number + an even number = an odd number; an odd number + an odd number = an even number.

Step 6. Summarize this information in a table:

+	Even	Odd
Even	Even	Odd
Odd	Odd	Even

Step 7. Prove deductively the relationships observed in step 5 by using the notation $2n$ and $2n + 1$ respectively for even and odd integers.

Step 8. Define a residue class modulo 2 as a set of integers that have the same remainder (either 0 or 1) when you divide by 2. Define addition of residue classes using the table developed in step 6.

Step 9. Link the additive group of residue classes modulo 2 to the additive group of the two-point clockface number system by winding the number line around the clock starting with the zero of the number line on the zero of the clock. Wind it like a string around a spool.

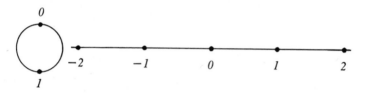

I have listed only some of the ways by which young children may be introduced to groups. Resourceful teachers will be able to think of many more.

Developing the concepts and skills that are necessary for studying and using groups

To prepare children for work with groups we have to cultivate the following concepts and skills:

1. The concept of binary operation.
2. The concept of closure.
3. The concept of identity element.
4. The concept of inverse.
5. The construction and use of a multiplication table.
6. The concept of associativity.
7. The concept of commutativity.
8. The meaning of exponents and skill in using them.

As you see, these are concepts and skills that already receive some attention in the elementary grades. What is needed to prepare for the curriculum of the future is an extension of these concepts and skills to wider domains. For example, in regard to item 1, the concept of binary operation, in addition to learning the operations with numbers, addition, subtraction, multiplication, and division, the children should begin to learn about operations with things that are not numbers, such as the combining of two motions, or the multiplication of two transformations. In regard to item 8, the meaning of exponents, in addition to learning how to use exponents that are positive integers, they should begin to learn the use of zero and of negative integers as exponents.

Items 2, 3, 4, 6 and 7 need no further comment. But there is an important aspect of item 5, the construction and use of a multiplication table, that deserves more attention than it usually gets. The members of a group serve as column labels and row labels for the multiplication table of the group. However, there is no prescribed order in which these labels should be listed. Any order may be used, and the order of the row labels need not be the same as the order of the column labels. For example, the multiplication table for the counting numbers 1, 2 and 3 may be written in any one of thirty-six ways, two of which are shown below. So there is not a unique way in

	1	2	3
1	1	2	3
2	2	4	6
3	3	6	9

	2	1	3
3	6	3	9
2	4	2	6
1	2	1	3

which a table may be written down. In general there are many different arrangements of the table, all conveying the same information. It is important that the children learn how to change a table from one of its possible arrangements to another. Given any table, it is always possible to rearrange it so that while the row labels and the column labels are given any desired order, the content of the table remains the same. This can be done by interchanging columns until the column labels have the desired order, and then interchanging the rows until the row labels have the desired order. We shall see an important use of this procedure in a few moments.

Providing experience with particular groups that are important for later study and applications

The following groups are particularly important, and can easily be introduced in the elementary grades:

1. For each integer n greater than or equal to 3, the group of those symmetries of a regular n-gon that are rotations about its center. This group is often called C_n, one of the family of cyclic groups.

2. For each integer n greater than or equal to 3, the group of *all* symmetries of a regular n-gon. This group is often called D_n, one of the family of dihedral groups.

3. For each integer n greater than or equal to 1, the group of all transformations of a set of n elements. This group is often called S_n, or the nth symmetric group.

4. The group of isometries of a straight line, that is, the group of those transformations of the line that leave the distances between points unchanged.

5. The group of isometries of the plane.

I shall comment briefly only on the last two.

An isometry of a straight line is either a translation or a reflection in a point. A translation is a motion that carries all points of the line the same distance in the same direction. A translation can be represented by an arrow. Combining translations is essentially the vector addition of arrows.

A reflection in a point P is the motion that carries each point A of the line to the point B such that P is the midpoint of AB. It is called a reflection in P because if a mirror were held perpendicular to the line at P, the reflection in the mirror of point A seems to be where point B is.

To study the isometries of a line, it is convenient to have two copies of the line, each drawn on a transparent strip of acetate, and placed over each other at first so that corresponding points coincide. Then each isometry can be made visible by actually moving one sheet over the other. Finally, it is convenient to have holes punched at some points on the line.

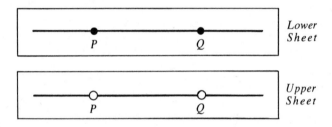

Then you can produce a reflection in a point P by inserting a pencil point through the hole at P and rotating the upper sheet 180 degrees. Using such acetate strips, the children can easily discover by themselves that if a reflection in P is followed by a reflection in Q, the effect is like a translation twice the distance PQ in the direction from P to Q.

An isometry of the plane is either a rotation about a point, or a translation, or a reflection in a line, or the product of a reflection in a line and a translation parallel to that line. Reflections in a line are of particular theoretical importance because every isometry of the plane can be represented as the product of at most three such reflections. They are of particular practical importance because they produce the bilateral symmetry that we encounter so often in nature and in art. To introduce young children to reflections in a line, Educational

Services Inc. has produced a set of mirror cards designed by Marion Walter. The basic problem posed by the mirror cards is that of placing a mirror on a pattern on one card so that the pattern united with its reflection in the mirror looks like the pattern on another card. Further details on the use of mirror cards are given in Miss Walter's article in the October 1966 issue of *The Arithmetic Teacher*.

Making the transition to formal study of abstract groups

This transition can be made in the sixth grade. Its basic ingredients are:

1. Formulation of the axioms for a group by abstraction from common properties of the specific groups with which the children have become familiar in the lower grades.

2. Establishment of some other properties by deductive reasoning from the axioms.

3. Introduction of the concept of isomorphism of groups.

4. Introduction of the concepts of subgroup, normal subgroup, cosets of a normal subgroup, and quotient modulo a normal subgroup.

Full details of this transition are given in my book, *Groups in the New Mathematics*. I shall take time here only to show how the concept of isomorphism can be presented so simply and concretely that it can be grasped by sixth-grade children.

Two groups are isomorphic, or have the same structure, if the table for one group is the same as the table for the other group except that it may, perhaps, be written in another language. In that case, with the help of a "dictionary" which matches each member of one group with one and only one member of the other group, it is possible to change one table into the other by translating it into the other language. For example, here are the tables for two different groups:

I. +	0	1	2	3
0	0	1	2	3
1	1	2	3	0
2	2	3	0	1
3	3	0	1	2

II. x	1	2	3	4
1	1	2	3	4
2	2	4	1	3
3	3	1	4	2
4	4	3	2	1

Table I is the table for the additive group of the four-point clockface number system. Table II is the table for the multiplicative group of the non-zero members of the five-point clockface number system. Let us translate Table I into another language by using this dictionary:

$$+ \longrightarrow \times$$
$$0 \longrightarrow 1$$
$$1 \longrightarrow 2$$
$$2 \longrightarrow 4$$
$$3 \longrightarrow 3$$

To make the translation, replace each entry in Table I by the symbol next to it in column 2 of the dictionary. The translated table looks like this:

Table I Translated:

x	1	2	4	3
1	1	2	4	3
2	2	4	3	1
4	4	3	1	2
3	3	1	2	4

To compare this table with Table II, we must first rearrange its columns and rows to give the column labels and the row labels the order 1, 2, 3, 4, which they have in Table II. When we interchange the 3 column and the 4 column, the translated table takes on this form:

x	1	2	3	4
1	1	2	3	4
2	2	4	1	3
4	4	3	2	1
3	3	1	4	2

When we next interchange the 3 row and the 4 row, the translated table takes on this form:

x	1	2	3	4
1	1	2	3	4
2	2	4	1	3
3	3	1	4	2
4	4	3	2	1

Now we can see at a glance that the translated table in this arrangement is exactly the same as Table II. Thus we have proved that the additive group of the four-point clockface number system is isomorphic to the multiplicative group of the non-zero members of the five-point clockface number system.

Using the group concept at the appropriate places in the curriculum for grades seven through ten

As I have already pointed out, the concept of a group will

be employed in these grades in the study of the number fields, in the study of the ring of integers and the ring of polynomials with real coefficients, in the study of Euclidean space as a vector space with an inner product, and in the study of Euclidean plane geometry as the geometry associated with a particular group of transformations of the plane, namely, the group of isometries. Further details about this step are given in the Cambridge Conference Report entitled *Goals for School Mathematics*.

What I have presented in this chapter are the bare bones of a proposed program for making the concept of a group a central idea in the mathematics curriculum for grades one to ten. It will take the cooperative effort of thousands of teachers in the classroom to put flesh on these bones and convert the program into a living reality.

Suggested Readings for Chapter 8

Adler, Irving, *Groups in the New Mathematics*. New York, The John Day Company.

————, *The New Mathematics*. New York, The John Day Company.

Educational Services Inc., *Goals for School Mathematics,* Report of the Cambridge Conference on School Mathematics. Boston, Houghton Mifflin Company.

Walter, Marion, "Mirror Cards." *The Arithmetic Teacher,* October 1966.

Index

185

Index

Index

Index

Index